Advantage Math

Grade 4

Table of Contents

Table of Contents

CREDITS

Concept Development: Kent Publishing Services, Inc.
Written by: Dawn Purney and Tremaine Gregory
Editor: Carla Hamaguchi
Designer/Production: Moonhee Pak/Carrie Carter
Illustrator: Corbin Hillam
Art Director: Tom Cochrane
Project Director: Carolea Williams

Introduction

The Advantage Math Series for grades 3–6 offers instruction and practice for key skills in each math strand recommended by the National Council for Teachers of Mathematics (NCTM), including

- numeration and number theory
- operations
- geometry
- measurement
- patterns, functions, and algebra
- data analysis and probability
- problem solving

Take a look at all the advantages this math series offers . . .

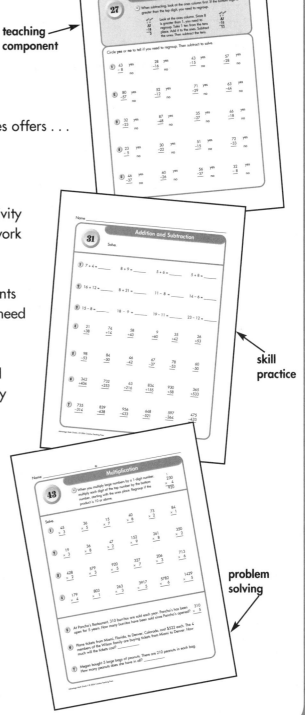

teaching component

skill practice

problem solving

Strong Skill Instruction

- The **teaching component** at the top of the activity pages provides the support students need to work through the book independently.

- Plenty of **skill practice** pages will ensure students master essential math computation skills they need to increase their math fluency.

- A **problem-solving strand** is woven within skill practice pages to offer students an opportunity to practice critical thinking skills.

Introduction

- **Mixed-practice pages** include a variety of math concepts on one workbook page. This challenges students to think through each problem rather than rely on a predictable format.

Assessment

- The "Take a Test Drive" pages provide practice using a **test-taking** format such as those included in national standardized and proficiency tests.

- The **tracking sheet** provides a place to record the number of right answers scored on each activity page. Use this as a motivational tool for students to strive for 100% accuracy.

Answer Key

- Answers for each page are provided at the back of the books to make **checking answers quick and easy.**

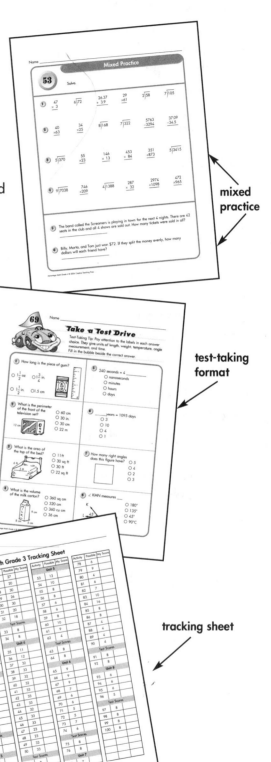

mixed practice

test-taking format

tracking sheet

Name _Jonathon Smith   12/28/13_

1

4 , 2 5 7 , 6 1 3

Answer the questions about the following number: 9,750,386

1 What value does the 7 have? _7 hundred thousands_

2 What is the place value of the 0? _0 thousands_

3 Which digit is in the tens place? _8 tens_

4 How many millions are there in this number? _9 millions_

Write the following numbers in standard form or word form.

5 Five thousand, four hundred seventy-nine _5,479_

6 Seven hundred two thousand, eight hundred ninety-nine _702,899_

7 Six million, four hundred fifty thousand, twenty-one _6,450,021_

8 2,356 _Two thousand, three hundred fifty-six_

9 1,209,411 _One million, two thousand nine, four hundred elven_

10 400,897 _Four hundred thousand, eight hundred ninety-seven_

11 What number has 5 tens, 3 thousands, 4 hundreds, and 2 ones? _3,452_

12 What number has nine ones, twelve thousands, and two hundreds? _12,209_

Advantage Math Grade 4 © 2004 Creative Teaching Press

Fractions

★ whole number $6\frac{5}{12}$ numerator = how many parts

denominator = how many parts make up a whole

fraction

Answer the question.

1

What fraction is shaded? _____

How many apples are there? _____

2

What fraction is shaded? _____

What fraction of the pans do the muffins fill? _____

Write the number in word form. Then shade in the correct amount.

3 $\frac{3}{10}$ _____

4 $4\frac{3}{4}$ _____

5 Brandi had five pages of stickers. She wanted to trade two pages. What fraction of her pages did Brandi keep?

_____

Decimals

Numbers after a decimal point tell about an amount smaller than a whole.

$4\dfrac{7}{100} = 4.07 =$ four and seven hundredths

ones tenths hundredths

Write the number in decimal and fraction form.

 1

_____ . _____   _____ . _____

Write the decimal in fraction form. Then, shade the correct amount.

2 2.8 _____

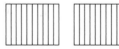

3 1.03 _____

4 Ryan cut his birthday cake into ten pieces. He ate one piece himself. How much of the cake did he eat?

_____

5 Ryan and his two sisters each ate a piece of cake. How much of the cake was left?

_____

Name _____

4 ⭐ Different fractions can be equal, or equivalent.

The fraction $\dfrac{2}{4}$ is $\dfrac{1}{2} \times 2$ or $\dfrac{1}{2} \times \dfrac{2}{2} = \dfrac{2}{4}$

To find equivalent fractions, multiply or divide both parts of a fraction by the same number.

$\dfrac{1}{2}$ $\dfrac{2}{4}$

$$\frac{2}{7} \times \frac{5}{5} = \frac{10}{35} \qquad\qquad \frac{3}{9} \div \frac{3}{3} = \frac{1}{3}$$

Shade the second shape to be equivalent to the first shape. Write the fractions.

1

$\dfrac{2}{5}$ ___   ___   ___

2

___   ___   ___   ___

Complete the patterns to write equivalent fractions. Remember to multiply or divide both parts of the fraction by the same number.

3 $\dfrac{1}{2}$ $\dfrac{2}{4}$ $\dfrac{3}{6}$ $\dfrac{4}{\rule{1em}{0.4pt}}$ ___   ___ $\dfrac{12}{18}$ $\dfrac{10}{15}$ $\dfrac{8}{\rule{1em}{0.4pt}}$ ___   ___

4 $\dfrac{3}{5}$ $\dfrac{6}{10}$ $\dfrac{9}{\rule{1em}{0.4pt}}$ ___   ___   ___ $\dfrac{8}{24}$ $\dfrac{7}{21}$ $\dfrac{6}{\rule{1em}{0.4pt}}$ ___   ___

Reducing Fractions

5

⭐ Reduce $\dfrac{10}{15}$ to its lowest terms.

Think: Can 10 and 15 be divided evenly by a whole number other than 1? (Yes, by 5.)
Divide both parts of the fraction by 5. $\dfrac{10}{15} \div \dfrac{5}{5} = \dfrac{2}{3}$
Think: Can the numerator and denominator be divided evenly by a whole number other than 1? (No.) $\dfrac{2}{3}$ is the lowest term of $\dfrac{10}{15}$.

Reduce each fraction to its lowest terms.

1 $\dfrac{8}{16} = \dfrac{1}{2}$ $\dfrac{3}{5} = \dfrac{3}{5}$ $\dfrac{9}{15} = $ ___ $\dfrac{30}{50} = $ ___

2 $\dfrac{4}{12} = $ ___ $\dfrac{2}{20} = $ ___ $\dfrac{7}{12} = $ ___ $\dfrac{6}{18} = $ ___

Cross out the fraction that is not equivalent to the others in the row. Circle the fraction that is in lowest terms.

3 $\dfrac{10}{15}$ $\dfrac{2}{3}$ $\dfrac{6}{9}$ $\dfrac{5}{10}$

4 $\dfrac{2}{8}$ $\dfrac{3}{15}$ $\dfrac{4}{16}$ $\dfrac{1}{4}$

5 $\dfrac{3}{6}$ $\dfrac{20}{40}$ $\dfrac{1}{2}$ $\dfrac{2}{10}$

6 $\dfrac{2}{5}$ $\dfrac{1}{10}$ $\dfrac{10}{25}$ $\dfrac{6}{15}$

Name _____

6 ⭐ Decimals can be written as fractions. Use the place value of the decimal to find the denominator of an equivalent fraction.

0.6 is six-tenths or $\frac{6}{10}$. Reduce $\frac{6}{10}$.

$$\frac{6}{10} \div \frac{2}{2} = \frac{3}{5} \qquad 0.6 = \frac{6}{10} = \frac{3}{5}$$

Write how much is shaded in decimal and in fraction form. Then reduce.

1

$0.5 =$ _____ $=$ _____

_____ $=$ _____ $=$ _____

2

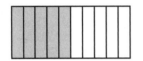

_____ $=$ _____ $=$ _____

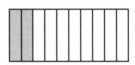

_____ $=$ _____ $=$ _____

Write the decimal as a fraction. Then reduce.

3 0.6 = _____ = _____   0.5 = _____ = _____

4 0.10 = _____ = _____   0.55 = _____ = _____

5 0.05 = _____ = _____   0.25 = _____ = _____

6 1.4 = 1 _____ = _____   3.8 = 3 _____ = _____

Comparing Numbers

7

⭐ Use >, <, and = signs to compare whole numbers.

$91 = 41 + 50$ 91 is equal to 41 + 50
$72 > 68$ 72 is greater than 68
$549 < 570$ 549 is less than 570

Complete the number sentence with the correct symbol: >, <, or =.

1. $20 + 5 \bigcirc 37$ $9 \bigcirc 0$

2. $58 \bigcirc 38 + 20$ $17 \bigcirc 42$

3. $348 \bigcirc 358$ $2{,}679 \bigcirc 3{,}104$

4. $87 \bigcirc 78$ $620 \bigcirc 531$

5. $1{,}254 \bigcirc 1{,}234$ $297 \bigcirc 277 + 30$

Write the numbers in order from lowest to highest.

6. 51, 112, 3, 25 + 27 _____

7. 8, 2 + 3, 11, 1 _____

8. 94, 27, 72, 50 + 43 _____

9. 28 + 10, 28, 14, 55 _____

10. 49; 149; 3,490; 3,049 _____

11. 71, 701, 17, 170, 107 _____

Comparing Numbers

8

⭐ $0.73 < 1$ Seventy-three hundredths is **less than** one.

Often, it is easier to compare numbers in the same form.
Change the decimal number to its equivalent fraction.

$2\frac{4}{10}$ ◯ 2.5 $2.5 = 2\frac{5}{10}$ $2\frac{4}{10} < 2\frac{5}{10}$ so, $2\frac{4}{10} < 2.5$

Complete the number sentence.

1 $3\frac{5}{6}$ ⬡> $3\frac{1}{6}$ 0.06 ◯ $\frac{6}{100}$

2 2.99 ◯ 3 $\frac{3}{4}$ ◯ 3

3 9.57 ◯ 9.75 $\frac{23}{100}$ ◯ 8.25

4 1.7 ◯ $1\frac{7}{100}$ $\frac{3}{4}$ ◯ 0.65

5 4.45 ◯ $4\frac{1}{2}$ $\frac{1}{2}$ ◯ 0.2

6 3.3 ◯ $3\frac{3}{10}$ $\frac{1}{2}$ ◯ 0.5

Write the fraction and the decimal.

7 How many of the books are shaded?

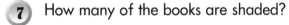

_____ = _____

How many of the cats have long fur?

_____ = _____

Number Line

9

⭐ A number line shows the order of numbers.

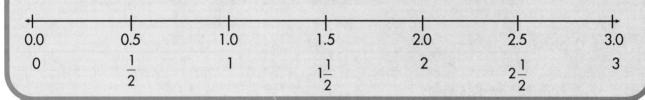

0.0	0.5	1.0	1.5	2.0	2.5	3.0
0	$\frac{1}{2}$	1	$1\frac{1}{2}$	2	$2\frac{1}{2}$	3

Complete the number line.

5.0   5.1   ☐   5.3   5.4   ☐   5.6   5.7   ☐   5.9   ☐

0   10   ☐   30   40   ☐   ☐   70   80   90   100

Complete the number line.

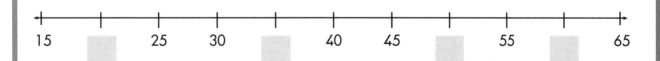

15   ☐   25   30   ☐   40   45   ☐   55   ☐   65

Complete the number line using fractions.

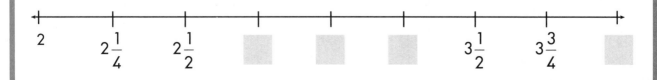

2   $2\frac{1}{4}$ $2\frac{1}{2}$ ☐   ☐   ☐ $3\frac{1}{2}$ $3\frac{3}{4}$ ☐

Name _____

10

Rewrite the number in word form.

1 510,200.3 _____

_____

$8\dfrac{17}{25}$ _____

Rewrite the number as a decimal, fraction, or mixed number.

2 Six hundred forty-eight thousand, nine hundred and sixty-seven tenths

_____

Twenty-one and three-fourths

_____

Shade the shape to show the fraction.

3 $\dfrac{3}{10}$ of the box

$\dfrac{5}{12}$ of the tennis balls

$\dfrac{1}{5}$ of the apples

Complete the number sentence.

4 0.8 ◯ 2.5

5 1,402 ◯ 1,357

$7\dfrac{4}{10}$ ◯ 7.4

783 ◯ 793

Complete the number line with fractions and decimals.

0 ———————————— 1 ———————————— 2 ———————————— 3

$\dfrac{1}{5}$ $\dfrac{2}{5}$ __ __ __ __ __

0.2 0.4 __ __ __ __ __

Name _____

Money Notation

11 ⭐ To write money, use decimals for amounts less than 1 dollar.

$1.93
dollar — cents

How much money is shown?

1. _____

2.    _____

3.    _____

4.   _____

Using the least number of bills and coins, write the number of each kind of bill and coin needed to make the amount.

$4.36		4				
$3.14						
$8.07						
$2.60						
$5.57						
$9.32						

Money Notation

Write the amounts, then add.

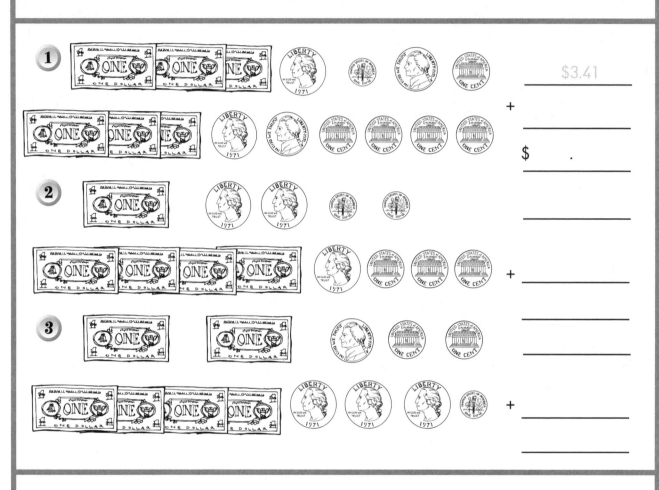

1. $3.41
   + _____
   $ _____ . _____

2. _____
   + _____

3. _____
   _____
   + _____
   _____

Write the problem, then solve.

4. Jessica had $2.43. Her mom gave her an allowance of $3.50. How much does Jessica have altogether?

   $2.43
   +$3.50
   _____

5. Matt had $5.78. He paid $3.25 for lunch. How much does Matt have now?

   $5.78
   −
   _____

6. Brittany had $4.80. She bought a set of baseball cards for $0.60. How much does she have now?

Expanded Form

13

⭐ The expanded form of a number shows the value of each digit.

Standard form: 8,630,712
Expanded form: 8,000,000 + 600,000 + 30,000 + 700 + 10 + 2

Rewrite the numbers in expanded form or standard form.

1 21,657 _____

2 540,031 _____

3 7,123,970 _____

4 6,700 _____

5 9,000,000 + 400 + 30 + 8 _____

6 2,000 + 100 + 8 _____

7 300,000 + 10,000 _____

8 70,000 + 9,000 + 50 + 4 _____

Answer the questions about the following number: 7,801,204.76

9 What value does the 2 represent? _____

10 How many millions are there? _____

11 What value does the 6 represent? _____

12 How many tens are there? _____

Roman Numerals

14

⭐ The Roman Numeral system uses I, V, and X to identify all whole numbers from 1 to 49. The symbols with the greatest value come first. If a lesser symbol comes before a greater, subtract the amount of the lesser from the greater. XIV stands for 14. X = 10, IV = 4 (1 less than 5).

19 in Roman numerals is XIX
The first X equals 10.
The IX equals 9.
Add: 10 + 9 = 19.

Standard Number System	Roman Number System
1	I
2	II
3	III
4	IV
5	V
6	VI
7	VII
8	VIII
9	IX
10	X
50	L
100	C
500	D
1,000	M

Convert into Roman numerals.

1. 6 _____   30 _____   3,000 _____

2. 29 _____   18 _____   502 _____

Convert into standard numbers.

3. CL _____   CD _____   XXXV _____

4. DC _____   XIV _____   XL _____

5. Add the totals to find the date on the statue.

M=_____ D=_____ C=_____ C=_____

L=_____ X=_____ X=_____ V=_____ I=_____

Year: _____

GEORGE WASHINGTON
MDCCLXXVI

Take a Test Drive

Test-Taking Tip: Fill in the bubble completely.

Fill in the bubble beside the correct answer.

1 Which number is six million, seven hundred two thousand, and thirty-one?

- ○ 6,072,310
- ○ 6,702,031
- ○ 6,720,301
- ○ 6,702,310

2 Which number is eight hundred and forty thousand, sixty-five, and twenty-three hundredths?

- ○ 804,650.03
- ○ 84,650.23
- ○ 840,065.23
- ○ 84,065.32

3 What fraction of the squares are shaded?

- ○ $\frac{60}{1000}$
- ○ $\frac{1}{6}$
- ○ $\frac{3}{5}$
- ○ 60

4 Which fraction is NOT equivalent to 0.75?

- ○ $\frac{7}{5}$
- ○ $\frac{3}{4}$
- ○ $\frac{75}{100}$
- ○ $\frac{15}{20}$

5 Choose the symbol that completes the number sentence.

$$2\frac{2}{3} \bigcirc 2\frac{2}{5}$$

- ○ <
- ○ >
- ○ V
- ○ =

6 Which symbol completes the number sentence?

$$33 \bigcirc 6+27$$

- ○ =
- ○ <
- ○ >
- ○ +

7 Which symbol completes the number sentence?

$$6.4 \bigcirc 6\frac{3}{10}$$

- ○ =
- ○ <
- ○ >
- ○ +

8 What is $\frac{4}{10}$ in lowest terms?

- ○ $\frac{4}{5}$
- ○ $\frac{1}{4}$
- ○ $\frac{8}{20}$
- ○ $\frac{2}{5}$

Name _____

Take a Test Drive

Fill in the bubble beside the correct answer.

---

1 How much money is shown?

○ 47¢
○ .87¢
○ $0.67
○ $0.87

---

5 Which is 5,601,084 in expanded form?

○ 5,000,000 + 600,000 + 1,000 + 800 + 40
○ 5,000 + 6,000 + 1,000 + 80 + 4
○ 5,000,000 + 600,000 + 1,000 + 80 + 4
○ 5,000,000 + 600,000 + 10,000 + 800 + 40

---

2 How much money is shown?

○ $50.48
○ $40.39
○ $20.35
○ $40.48

---

6 Which is 400,000 + 200 + 60 + 7 in standard form?

○ 400,267
○ 4,267
○ 40,267
○ 400,260

---

3 How much of the box is shaded?

○ 0.27
○ 0.027
○ 27
○ $\frac{27}{10}$

---

7 Christian had $3.48. He spent $2.30 for a book. How much does he have now?

○ $1.18
○ $2.30
○ $3.10
○ $5.78

---

4 Which number is XC?

○ 90
○ 110
○ 1000
○ 10100

---

8 Which number is 16?

○ XIV
○ XVI
○ LIV
○ MVI

Rounding

17

⭐ Round 753 to the nearest ten.
Use the digit in the place to the right of the tens.
If it is < 5 (less than 5) ➤ round **DOWN**
If it is ≥ 5 (greater than or equal to 5)➤ round **UP**
Since 3 < 5, round down to the nearest ten ➤ 50
750

Round 753 to the nearest hundred.
Use the digit in the place to the right of the hundreds.
Since 5 = 5, round up to the nearest hundred ➤ 800
800

Round.

1 36 to the nearest ten _____   2,289 to the nearest thousand _____

2 531 to the nearest ten _____   6,511 to the nearest thousand _____

3 8,703 to the nearest hundred _____   65 to the nearest ten _____

4 781 to the nearest hundred _____   96,730 to the nearest thousand _____

5 436 to the nearest hundred _____   798 to the nearest thousand _____

6 There are 319 animals in the zoo. If you round to the nearest hundred, about how many animals are there? _____

7 A mile is 5280 feet long. Jenny jogged 1 mile. Round the number of feet she jogged to the nearest hundred. _____

8 Andrew has 61 baseball cards in his collection. Danny has 33. If the two friends combine their collections, about how many cards will they have in all? Round your answer to the nearest ten. _____

Rounding

18

⭐ Round 690,891 to the nearest hundred thousand.
To the right of the hundred thousands place is a 9.
9 > 5, so round up.
700,000

Round.

1 35,304 to the nearest thousand
_____

815,601 to the nearest hundred thousand
_____

2 703,811 to the nearest ten thousand
_____

51,259 to the nearest hundred
_____

3 6,090 to the nearest hundred
_____

976,508 to the nearest ten
_____

4 570,622 to the nearest ten thousand
_____

152,009 to the nearest hundred thousand
_____

5 42,782 to the nearest ten thousand
_____

73,308 to the nearest hundred
_____

6 708,093 to the nearest thousand
_____

71,837 to the nearest ten thousand
_____

7 Nick learned that there are 548,190 people in the town where he lives. What is the population of Nick's town rounded to the nearest hundred thousand? _____

8 On Friday night at Kendall Stadium, 24,728 people attended the football game. 15,271 attended the Saturday night game. How many attended football games over the two days? Round your answer to the nearest ten thousand. _____

Factors and Multiples

19

⭐ A **factor** is a number that divides evenly into another number.
Factors of 6: 1, 2, 3, 6
$6 \div 6 = 1$
$6 \div 3 = 2$
$6 \div 2 = 3$
$6 \div 1 = 6$

A **multiple** is a number that is multiplied by something to get a number that is equal or greater.
Multiples of 6: 6, 12, 18, 24, 30, 36, 42, 48, 54, 60, and so on

Answer the questions using factors and multiples.

1. Is 99 a multiple of 9? _____   Is 7 a factor of 50? _____

2. Is 62 a multiple of 6? _____   Is 10 a factor of 100? _____

3. Is 48 a factor of 8? _____   Is 48 a multiple of 8? _____

4. Is 72 a factor of 9? _____   Is 36 a multiple of 9? _____

5. List all 8 factors for 30. _____

6. List all 11 multiples for 9 (up to 100).

   _____

7. Sarah bought stickers for 6 of her friends. She was able to divide the stickers evenly. Circle the number of stickers that Sarah could have bought.   61   26   36   53

8. Fillip helped his grandmother move. He put her book collection in boxes. If she has 78 books and 8 boxes, will Fillip be able to put an equal number of books in each box? Explain.

   _____

Factors and Multiples

20

⭐ What is the greatest common factor for 4 and 6?
factors of 4: 1, 2, 4 (1 x 4, 2 x 2)
factors of 6: 1, 2, 3, 6 (1 x 6, 2 x 3)
1 and 2 are common factors, 2 is the greatest of these.

What is the least common multiple for 4 and 9?
multiples of 4: 4, 8, 12, 16, 20, 24, 28, 32, 36, 40, . . .
multiples of 9: 9, 18, 27, 36, . . .
36 is the lowest common multiple.

Answer the questions using factors and multiples.

1. List all the factors of 12. _____

2. List the common factors for 6 and 12. _____

3. What is the greatest common factor for 3 and 4? _____

4. What is the greatest common factor for 8 and 7? _____

5. What is the greatest common factor for 6 and 9? _____

6. List the first 10 multiples of 8. _____

7. List two common multiples of 8 and 6. _____

8. What is the least common multiple for 12 and 4? _____

9. What is the least common multiple for 20 and 30? _____

10. What is the least common multiple for 8 and 6? _____

11. Zeke has to read 42 pages for school. He wants to read an equal number of pages each day. If he reads 8 pages today, will he be able to read an equal number of pages each day until he finishes? Explain. _____

12. Marianna wants to separate her 25 math flash cards into equal groups of 5. Will she be able to do this? Explain. _____

Multiples

21

★ When counting by multiples of 10, you don't have to add ten every time. Just add 1 to the number in the tens place.

10, 20, 30, 40, 50, . . .   OR   110, 120, 130, 140, 150, . . .

Remember, when you're counting by tens, only the number in the tens place changes.

Complete the patterns using multiples of 10.

1 40, 50, _____, 70   130, _____, 150, 160

2 270, _____, 290, 300   780, 790, _____, 810

3 2,370; 2,380; _____; 2,400   5,430; 5,440; 5,450; _____

4 440, _____   90, _____   _____, 230

5 1,020; _____   _____, 310   260, _____

6 _____, 80   700, _____   _____; 1,000

7 Kate is counting the miles that her family will travel this summer by tens. She has gotten to 120 miles, but she can't remember what the next number should be. Help Kate by writing what comes after 120, counting by tens. _____

8 Darrel is counting the tickets that he has sold for the winter play by 10. So far he has gotten to 60 tickets. What will be the next number in his count? _____

Multiples

22

⭐ Counting by multiples of one hundred:

100, 200, 300, 400, . . . OR 1,300; 1,400; 1,500; 1,600; . . .

Counting by thousands:

1,000; 2,000; 3,000; 4,000; . . . OR 3,111; 4,111; 5,111; 6,111; . . .

Complete the pattern.

1 400, 500, _____, 700   7,000; _____; 9,000; 10,000

2 1,700; _____; 1,900; 2,000   62,000; 63,000; 64,000; _____

3 4,850; 4,950; _____; 5,150   8,000; _____; 10,000; 11,000

Cross out the number that is wrong. Write the number that should be in its place.

4 10, 20, 21, 40, 50 _____

5 315, 415, 515, 616 _____

6 1,100; 2,000; 3,000; 4,000 _____

7 Mrs. Vasquez is counting years by 100. She just reached 1,600. What will be the next number?

_____

8 Carlos is practicing counting by thousands. He just got to 5,000, and he's stuck. Help Carlos by writing the next number after 5,000.

_____

Rules of Divisibility

23

⭐ Every number is divisible by (can be divided by) its factors.

Rules can help you figure out if a number is divisible by 2 or 3.

All numbers that are divisible by 2 **end in even numbers.**
Is 54 divisible by 2? Since 54 ends in an even number (4), it is divisible by 2.

For all numbers that are divisible by 3, the **sum of the digits is divisible by 3.** Is 65 divisible by 3? Since 6 + 5 = 11 and 11 is not divisible by 3, 65 is not divisible by 3.

Answer the questions about divisibility.

1 Is 87 divisible by 2?

_____

Is 96 divisible by 3?

_____

2 Is 462 divisible by 2?

_____

Is 323 divisible by 3?

_____

3 Is 78 divisible by 2, 3, or both?

_____

Is 42 divisible by 2, 3, or both?

_____

4 Is 136 divisible by 2, 3, or both?

_____

Is 36 divisible by 2, 3, or both?

_____

5 Erik wants to divide the cherries he picked evenly between his three sisters. If he picked 38 cherries will he be able to do this? _____

6 Mrs. O'Brien wants to put the 25 candles she bought into 2 boxes. Will she be able to put an equal number of candles in each box? _____

Name _____

Rules of Divisibility

24

⭐ More rules of divisibility:
If a number is divisible by 5, **it ends in 0 or 5.**
If a number is divisible by 9, **the sum of the digits is divisible by 9.**
If a number is divisible by 10, **it ends in 0.**

Answer the following questions about the divisibility of 5, 9, and 10.

1 Is 17,740 divisible by 10? _____   Is 37 divisible by 5? _____

2 Is 891 divisible by 9? _____   Is 60 divisible by 5? _____

3 Which number is divisible by 10?   Which number is divisible by 9?
785   330   201   59   49   117   58   123

4 Which number is divisible by 5?   Which number is divisible by 9?
105   56   663   3,001   727   2,809   836   6,021

5 Which number is NOT divisible by 5?   Which number is NOT divisible by 9?
15   30   51   65   18   29   99   108

6 Jackie's Movie Shop just got in 68 new videos. If Jackie wants to put 5 videos on a shelf with none leftover, will she be able to do this? _____

7 Pablo packed his 45 books into boxes. If he put an equal number of books into each box, how many books did he pack in each box? Explain.

_____

_____

Name _____

Perfect Squares

25

When a number is multiplied by itself, the product is called a **perfect square.**

Example: 9 x 9 = 81
This box is a perfect square, all four sides are equal.

Identify the perfect square represented by each box.

1

_____ x _____ = _____   _____ x _____ = _____

2

_____ x _____ = _____   _____ x _____ = _____

Now draw the perfect squares yourself.

3

4 x 4 = _____   8 x 8 = _____   3 x 3 = _____

4

6 x 6 = _____   2 x 2 = _____   11 x 11 = _____

Perfect Squares

26

List the perfect square.

1 2 _____   3 _____   4 _____   5 _____

2 6 _____   7 _____   8 _____   9 _____

Solve. Draw a picture to help you find the answer.

3 Tiffany made a quilt. She wanted the quilt to be a perfect square with at least 80 patches. How many patches could the quilt have on each side?

_____

4 Sean and Mary put a new tile floor in their kitchen. The kitchen is perfectly square and 7 tiles fit on one side. How many tiles will they have to buy total to tile the entire floor?

_____

5 Chelsey hung pictures on her wall. She hung 9 pictures in all. Since she arranged the pictures to be in a perfect square pattern, how many did she put on a side?

_____

6 Steve made a square wall with blocks in his backyard. If he put 6 blocks down as the base of the wall, how many blocks will he end up using? _____

Name _____

27

Solve.

1. What is 384 rounded to the nearest ten? _____

2. What is 57,519 rounded to the nearest thousand? _____

3. What is 57,519 rounded to the nearest hundred? _____

4. Peggy counted 525 sunflowers in the field. Rounding to the nearest hundred, about how many sunflowers did Peggy see? _____

5. List all of the factors of 20. Hint: there are 6. _____

6. Is 4 a factor of 60? _____

7. What is the greatest common factor for 20 and 16? _____

8. What is the least common multiple for 5 and 6? _____

9. Is 18 a multiple of 4? _____

10. What numbers are missing? 110, 120, _____, 140, _____

11. If there are 24 dogs that need to be walked and 8 dog walkers to walk them, will each dog walker be walking an equal number of dogs? _____

12. Fill in the blanks with the missing multiples of 1000.
    2,030; _____; _____; 5,030; _____; 7,030

Name _____

28

Solve.

1. What is the next multiple of 1,000 after 9,000? _____

2. 110, 120, 130, 140
   These numbers are all multiples of what number? _____

3. Is 54 divisible by 3, 5, or both? _____

4. Write a number less than 10 that is a factor of 72. _____

5. Write the perfect square of 9. _____

6. What is the greatest common factor for 32 and 24? _____

7. What is the least common multiple for 9 and 3? _____

8. Cross out the number that is NOT divisible by 5.
   15   30   56   90

9. Cross out the number that is NOT divisible by 9.
   99   135   360   39

10. Which box shows the perfect square for 4?

11. In order to fit all of the boxes in the moving truck, Mr. Palzeri wants to stack them in a perfect square. If he has 36 boxes, draw a picture of the way he should stack them.

Take a Test Drive

Test-Taking Tip: Always read the questions and the answers carefully. Don't rush.

Fill in the bubble beside the correct answer.

1 Which number is rounded to the nearest 1000?
- ○ 60,400
- ○ 405,000
- ○ 2,200
- ○ 300

2 There are 652,710 people in Becky's city. If she rounds the population to the nearest hundred thousand, what will the estimated population be?
- ○ 700,000
- ○ 652,700
- ○ 600,000
- ○ 653,000

3 Which number is NOT rounded to the nearest ten?
- ○ 200
- ○ 3040
- ○ 120,500
- ○ 705

4 The factors of 80 include all of the following numbers EXCEPT _____.
- ○ 8
- ○ 10
- ○ 4
- ○ 9

5 3, 4, and 5 are all factors of which number?
- ○ 75
- ○ 60
- ○ 56
- ○ 48

6 Nico found 86 lost golf balls. If 9 balls fit in a tube, will Nico be able to put an equal number of balls in each tube?
- ○ Yes, 9 tubes with 9 balls in each
- ○ No, 10 tubes with 9 balls and one with 5
- ○ No, 9 tubes with 9 balls and one with 5
- ○ Yes, 10 tubes with 9 balls in each

7 What is the next number in the series? 1,440; 1,450; 1,460; _____
- ○ 1,470
- ○ 1,400
- ○ 1,500
- ○ 1,740

8 Which set of numbers increases by multiples of 10,000?
- ○ 92,000; 93,000; 94,000
- ○ 200,000; 300,000; 400,000
- ○ 560,000; 670,000; 780,000
- ○ 75,000; 85,000; 95,000

Name _____

Take a Test Drive

Fill in the bubble beside the correct answer.

---

1 54 is divisible by all of the numbers EXCEPT _____.

- ○ 2
- ○ 3
- ○ 5
- ○ 9

2 Which is the least common multiple for 5 and 10?

- ○ 5
- ○ 10
- ○ 20
- ○ 50

3 All of the numbers are divisible by 9 EXCEPT _____.

- ○ 49
- ○ 54
- ○ 45
- ○ 81

4 A number that is divisible by 2 could end in _____.

- ○ 3
- ○ 9
- ○ 5
- ○ 4

5 What is the greatest common factor for 9 and 6?

- ○ 1
- ○ 3
- ○ 6
- ○ 9

6 Which of the numbers is a perfect square?

- ○ 68
- ○ 49
- ○ 34
- ○ 97

7 Which shows all the factors for 10?

- ○ 2, 5
- ○ 1, 2, 5, 10
- ○ 5, 10, 15, 20, 25
- ○ 10, 20, 30, 40, 50

8 Mrs. Sakamoto organized her stamp collection. Her pages have squares of stamps with 5 stamps across the top and 5 stamps down the side. How many stamps are on each page?

- ○ 15
- ○ 25
- ○ 20
- ○ 36

Addition and Subtraction

31

Solve.

1 7 + 4 = _____   8 + 9 = _____   5 + 6 = _____   5 + 8 = _____

2 16 + 12 = _____   8 + 21 = _____   11 − 8 = _____   14 − 6 = _____

3 15 − 8 = _____   18 − 9 = _____   19 − 11 = _____   23 − 12 = _____

4
$$21 \\ +38$$ $$74 \\ +14$$ $$58 \\ +40$$ $$9 \\ +60$$ $$35 \\ +42$$ $$26 \\ +53$$

5
$$98 \\ -53$$ $$84 \\ -50$$ $$46 \\ -42$$ $$67 \\ -37$$ $$78 \\ -53$$ $$60 \\ -50$$

6
$$342 \\ +406$$ $$732 \\ +253$$ $$63 \\ +216$$ $$834 \\ +155$$ $$930 \\ +58$$ $$365 \\ +533$$

7
$$735 \\ -314$$ $$839 \\ -638$$ $$956 \\ -433$$ $$648 \\ -521$$ $$597 \\ -364$$ $$475 \\ -433$$

Addition and Subtraction

32

⭐ When digits in one place add up to 10 or more, regroup into the next place.

$$\begin{array}{r} 1 \\ 358 \\ +423 \\ \hline 781 \end{array}$$

When a digit to subtract is greater than the digit to subtract from, borrow from the next highest place.

$$\begin{array}{r} 1\ 10 \\ 42\cancel{0} \\ -203 \\ \hline 217 \end{array}$$

Solve. Regroup or borrow when needed.

1)

72	46	56	33	54	78
+19	+28	+34	+18	+35	+ 7

2)

87	56	63	70	67	54
−29	−43	−18	−25	−58	−37

3)

472	729	572	492	197	394
+283	+231	+208	+285	+ 85	+125

4)

492	237	729	603	972	530
−327	− 46	−483	−312	−718	−128

5) There are 86 students at lunch. If 19 go outside, how many are left? _____

6) During lunchtime, 86 students are in the lunchroom. Then, 95 more students join them. How many students are in the lunchroom altogether? _____

Addition and Subtraction

33

⭐ You may have to regroup more than once.

```
  1 1
 37,324
+13,935
───────
 51,259
```

You may need to borrow more than once.

```
 6 11 13
 7,2̶3̶5
-2,394
───────
 4,841
```

Solve. Regroup or borrow when needed.

1

472	270	623	823	734	387
+298	+357	+175	+ 59	+293	+309

2

582	492	808	573	734	290
−328	−387	−236	−206	−563	−185

3

3,476	5,093	19,872	27,439	52,745	7,483
+2,394	+4,423	+2,146	+31,726	+34,657	+63,034

4

7,862	8,538	46,032	47,375	84,057	62,784
− 990	−5,439	− 5,822	−32,194	−26,155	−32,893

5 At the first Open House, 349 parents attended. At the second Open House, 418 parents attended. How many more parents came to the second Open House? _____

6 The fourth graders performed for 367 students. Then they performed for 95 parents. How many people saw them perform? _____

Addition of Decimals

34

⭐ Adding decimals is like adding whole numbers, just remember to place the decimal point correctly in the sum. Add a 0 in the hundredths place as a placeholder, if necessary.

$$\begin{array}{r} 1 \\ 5.62 \\ +13.80 \\ \hline 19.42 \end{array}$$

Add. Regroup if needed.

1
$$\begin{array}{r} 10.57 \\ +\ 1.33 \\ \hline \end{array}$$
$$\begin{array}{r} 23.6 \\ +\ 8.15 \\ \hline \end{array}$$
$$\begin{array}{r} 6.72 \\ +3.19 \\ \hline \end{array}$$
$$\begin{array}{r} 8.13 \\ +17.04 \\ \hline \end{array}$$
$$\begin{array}{r} 28.3 \\ +\ 1.26 \\ \hline \end{array}$$
$$\begin{array}{r} 4.67 \\ +31.82 \\ \hline \end{array}$$

2
$$\begin{array}{r} 19.04 \\ +20.57 \\ \hline \end{array}$$
$$\begin{array}{r} 8.03 \\ +9.4 \\ \hline \end{array}$$
$$\begin{array}{r} 24.03 \\ +36.97 \\ \hline \end{array}$$
$$\begin{array}{r} 15.26 \\ +42.3 \\ \hline \end{array}$$
$$\begin{array}{r} 38.35 \\ +21.96 \\ \hline \end{array}$$
$$\begin{array}{r} 52.67 \\ +27.09 \\ \hline \end{array}$$

3
$$\begin{array}{r} 20.73 \\ +\ 1.8 \\ \hline \end{array}$$
$$\begin{array}{r} 15.01 \\ +\ 7.83 \\ \hline \end{array}$$
$$\begin{array}{r} 47.8 \\ +21.65 \\ \hline \end{array}$$
$$\begin{array}{r} 18.71 \\ +50.09 \\ \hline \end{array}$$
$$\begin{array}{r} 0.27 \\ +0.43 \\ \hline \end{array}$$
$$\begin{array}{r} 1.63 \\ +0.6 \\ \hline \end{array}$$

4 Bill bought a jar of peanut butter for $3.27 and some jelly for $2.65. How much did he spend in all? _____

5 Jasmine ran 4.75 miles during track practice today. Julie ran 3.45 miles. How many miles did the two girls run in all? _____

6 Sparky ate 0.85 pound of dog food on Tuesday and 0.65 pound of food on Wednesday. How much did Sparky eat in the 2 days? _____

Subtraction of Decimals

35

⭐ To subtract decimals, remember to include the decimal point. Use a 0 as a placeholder, if needed.

$$
\begin{array}{r}
\overset{5\ 10}{5\ 4.\cancel{6}\cancel{0}} \\
-\ 4.23 \\
\hline
50.37
\end{array}
$$

Subtract. Use placeholders and borrow, if needed.

1
9.07 −2.45	74.9 − 3.81	81.37 − 4.1	62.81 − 41.73	22.5 − 1.24	13.09 − 2.15

2
9.86 −4.35	47.61 −38.4	52.37 −31.84	24.03 −10.72	31.5 −20.09	82.42 −64.3

3
10.01 − 7.21	91.82 −37.63	45.23 −45.07	76.18 − 8.9	26.08 −14.1	63.7 −51.03

4 Trey bought a pair of pants that were on sale for $24.50. If the regular price is $30.95, how much did he save? _____

5 Lily is 1.74 meters tall, and Tim is 1.82 meters tall. How much taller is Tim? _____

6 Nick wants to wrestle in the weight class 69.99 pounds and under. He weighs 73.5 pounds. How much weight does he have to lose? _____

Advantage Math Grade 4 © 2004 Creative Teaching Press

Name _____

36

⭐ When you add or subtract fractions with the same denominators, simply add or subtract the numerators. Keep the denominator the same.

$$\frac{7}{8} + \frac{3}{8} = \frac{10}{8} = 1\frac{2}{8} = 1\frac{1}{4} \qquad \frac{9}{10} - \frac{5}{10} = \frac{4}{10} = \frac{2}{5}$$

Add. Change the sum to a mixed number in lowest terms.

1. $\frac{6}{7} + \frac{5}{7} = \frac{}{7} = \quad \frac{}{7}$ $\qquad \frac{5}{10} + \frac{9}{10} = \frac{}{10} = \quad \frac{}{10} =$ _____

2. $\frac{8}{9} + \frac{4}{9} = \frac{}{9} = \quad \frac{}{9} =$ _____ $\qquad \frac{13}{16} + \frac{7}{16} = \frac{}{16} = \quad \frac{}{16} =$ _____

3. $\frac{5}{6} + \frac{4}{6} =$ _____ $\qquad \frac{8}{11} + \frac{4}{11} =$ _____

4. $\frac{15}{21} - \frac{8}{21} =$ _____ $\qquad \frac{14}{18} - \frac{12}{18} =$ _____

5. $\frac{11}{13} - \frac{5}{13} =$ _____ $\qquad \frac{8}{9} - \frac{2}{9} =$ _____

6. $\frac{16}{20} - \frac{6}{20} =$ _____ $\qquad \frac{14}{15} - \frac{4}{15} =$ _____

7. $\frac{14}{49} - \frac{7}{49} =$ _____ $\qquad \frac{5}{10} - \frac{4}{10} =$ _____

Name _____

Addition and Subtraction of Fractions

37

⭐ When you add and subtract fractions, find the common denominator if the denominators are not the same. A common denominator is a multiple of both denominators.

$$\frac{3}{4}+\frac{5}{8}=$$

Since 8 is a multiple of 4, 8 is the common denominator. $4 \times 2 = 8$. Multiply both the numerator and the denominator of the fraction 3/4 by 2 to get an equivalent fraction.

$$\frac{3\times 2}{4\times 2}=\frac{6}{8}$$

Now add the numerators.

$$\frac{6}{8}+\frac{5}{8}=\frac{11}{8}$$

Change the fraction to a mixed number. Divide the numerator by the denominator. $11 \div 8 = 1$ R3

$$1\frac{3}{8}$$

Solve.

1 $\dfrac{2}{3}+\dfrac{3}{4}=\dfrac{(2\times\ \ )}{(3\times\ \ )}+\dfrac{(3\times\ \ )}{(4\times\ \ )}=\dfrac{\ \ }{12}=$ _____ = _____

2 $\dfrac{7}{8}-\dfrac{1}{4}=\dfrac{7}{8}-\dfrac{(1\times\ \ )}{(4\times\ \ )}=$ _____

3 $\dfrac{1}{3}+\dfrac{1}{6}=$ _____ $\dfrac{11}{12}-\dfrac{1}{4}=$ _____

4 $\dfrac{2}{5}+\dfrac{3}{5}=$ _____ $\dfrac{4}{5}-\dfrac{3}{10}=$ _____

5 Spot the Cat needs ½ of a cup of water daily. Farfo the Dog needs ⅘ of a cup of water daily. Between the two animals, how much water is needed?

_____

6 Carolina and Juan are reading the same book. Carolina has read ⅔ of the book and Juan has read ⅓ of the book. How much less of the book has Juan read?

_____

Number Properties

38

⭐ Addition:

Identity Property: when you add zero to any number, the answer is the number you started with. Example: $14 + 0 = 14$

Commutative Property: switch the numbers in an addition problem, and the sum does not change. Example: $3 + 7 = 7 + 3$

Associative Property: group different numbers in an addition problem, and the sum does not change. Example: $(2 + 8) + 6 = 2 + (8 + 6)$

Multiplication:

Zero Property: when you multiply any number by zero, the product is zero. Example: $18 \times 0 = 0$

Identity Property: when you multiply any number by one, the product is that number. Example: $12 \times 1 = 12$

Commutative Property: group different numbers in a multiplication problem, and the product does not change. Example: $5 \times 4 = 4 \times 5$

Associative Property: group different numbers in a multiplication problem, and the product does not change. Example: $(7 \times 9) \times 2 = 7 \times (9 \times 2)$

Distributive Property: multiplying a number by the sum of two other numbers is the same as adding the products of the number and the two summed numbers. Example: $3(4 + 5) = (3 \times 4) + (3 \times 5)$

Complete the number sentence. Write the property you used.

1 $5 \times 0 = \underline{0}$ zero property of multiplication

2 $4 + 8 = \underline{} + 4$ _____

3 $(7 + 8) + 1 = 7 + (\underline{} + 1)$ _____

4 $20 \times \underline{} = 20$ _____

5 $8 (3 + 6) = (\underline{} \times 3) + (8 \times \underline{})$ _____

6 $(2 \times 4) \times 6 = 2 \times (\underline{} \times 6)$ _____

7 $13 + \underline{} = 13$ _____

8 $21 \times 6 = \underline{} \times 21$ _____

Multiplication Facts

39

Solve.

1. _____ x 5 = 20   6 x _____ = 18   7 x 7 = _____   8 x _____ = 32

2. 7 x 8 = _____   9 x 3 = _____   4 x 3 = _____   5 x 5 = _____

3.
8	2	10	7	1	6
×8	×6	× 3	×5	×9	×4

4.
4	1	3	7	5	8
×6	×0	×7	×9	×5	×5

5.
8	9	6	3	0	5
×6	×4	×7	×8	×4	×9

6. Daniel has 9 packs of baseball cards. There are 8 cards in each pack. How many cards does Daniel have? _____

7. Jessica made sure that each blueberry pancake she made had 10 blueberries. If Jessica made 9 pancakes, how many blueberries did she use? _____

8. If a squirrel stored 6 acorns per day for 7 days, how many acorns did it have total? _____

Division Facts

40

Solve.

1) $20 \div \underline{\hspace{1cm}} = 5$ $18 \div 6 = \underline{\hspace{1cm}}$ $64 \div 8 = \underline{\hspace{1cm}}$ $45 \div \underline{\hspace{1cm}} = 9$

2) $32 \div \underline{\hspace{1cm}} = 8$ $42 \div 7 = \underline{\hspace{1cm}}$ $\underline{\hspace{1cm}} \div 5 = 5$ $77 \div 11 = \underline{\hspace{1cm}}$

3) $7\overline{)56}$ $9\overline{)81}$ $6\overline{)36}$ $5\overline{)50}$ $7\overline{)7}$ $3\overline{)27}$

4) $6\overline{)18}$ $2\overline{)16}$ $7\overline{)49}$ $10\overline{)80}$ $8\overline{)32}$ $5\overline{)45}$

5) $9\overline{)72}$ $7\overline{)35}$ $8\overline{)56}$ $6\overline{)24}$ $3\overline{)30}$ $3\overline{)24}$

6) All 5 people in the Jackson family went to the movies. If Mr. Jackson paid $25 for everyone, how much did each ticket cost? _____

7) Jack read a 100-page book. If he read 10 pages each day, how many days did it take Jack to read the book? _____

8) Maya had 54 pictures for her scrapbook. If she put 6 pictures on each page, how many pages did Maya use? _____

Mixed Practice

41

Solve.

1 $\dfrac{12}{16} - \dfrac{6}{16} =$ _____ $\dfrac{13}{14} - \dfrac{8}{14} =$ _____

2

724	265	628	327	418	832
+135	+ 79	−307	−129	+367	−652

3

55.3	1.27	86.04	39.0	42,320	83,403
+26.05	+16.9	−73.81	−13.7	−27,492	− 7,539

4 $\dfrac{1}{3} + \dfrac{1}{3} =$ _____ $\dfrac{1}{8} + \dfrac{3}{8} =$ _____

5 $\dfrac{3}{4} - \dfrac{1}{2} =$ _____ $\dfrac{4}{5} - \dfrac{2}{3} =$ _____

6 $\dfrac{1}{4} + \dfrac{1}{6} =$ _____ $\dfrac{3}{4} + \dfrac{1}{8} =$ _____

Mixed Practice

42

Multiply or divide. Change your answer to a mixed fraction in lowest terms, if necessary.

1 $6 \times 8 =$ _____   _____ $\times \ 5 = 45$ $24 \div$ _____ $= 3$ $12 \div 3 =$ _____

2 $3 \times 7 =$ _____ $2 \times 6 =$ _____ $35 \div 5 =$ _____ $16 \div 4 =$ _____

3
$$\begin{array}{r} 10 \\ \times \ 8 \\ \hline \end{array}$$
$7\overline{)42}$
$$\begin{array}{r} 6 \\ \times 6 \\ \hline \end{array}$$
$4\overline{)8}$
$$\begin{array}{r} 3 \\ \times 9 \\ \hline \end{array}$$
$5\overline{)20}$

4
$11\overline{)99}$
$$\begin{array}{r} 7 \\ \times 4 \\ \hline \end{array}$$
$3\overline{)30}$
$$\begin{array}{r} 9 \\ \times 0 \\ \hline \end{array}$$
$5\overline{)5}$
$$\begin{array}{r} 10 \\ \times \ 6 \\ \hline \end{array}$$

Complete the equation. Then write the letter of the rule you used.

5 $5 + 3 =$ _____ $+ 5$ _____

   $9 + 0 =$ _____   _____

   $1 \times 7 =$ _____   _____

   $6 \times 4 = 4 \times$ _____   _____

   $2 \times 0 =$ _____   _____

Commutative Property
Identity Property
Zero Property

Multiplication

43

⭐ When you multiply large numbers by a 1-digit number, multiply each digit of the top number by the bottom number, starting with the ones place. Regroup if the product is 10 or above.

$$\begin{array}{r} {\scriptstyle 1} \\ 230 \\ \times\ \ 4 \\ \hline 920 \end{array}$$

Solve.

1
$$\begin{array}{r} 45 \\ \times\ 3 \\ \hline \end{array} \qquad \begin{array}{r} 36 \\ \times\ 5 \\ \hline \end{array} \qquad \begin{array}{r} 15 \\ \times\ 7 \\ \hline \end{array} \qquad \begin{array}{r} 40 \\ \times\ 8 \\ \hline \end{array} \qquad \begin{array}{r} 73 \\ \times\ 2 \\ \hline \end{array} \qquad \begin{array}{r} 84 \\ \times\ 1 \\ \hline \end{array}$$

2
$$\begin{array}{r} 19 \\ \times\ 3 \\ \hline \end{array} \qquad \begin{array}{r} 36 \\ \times\ 8 \\ \hline \end{array} \qquad \begin{array}{r} 47 \\ \times\ 2 \\ \hline \end{array} \qquad \begin{array}{r} 152 \\ \times\ 9 \\ \hline \end{array} \qquad \begin{array}{r} 261 \\ \times\ 8 \\ \hline \end{array} \qquad \begin{array}{r} 350 \\ \times\ 2 \\ \hline \end{array}$$

3
$$\begin{array}{r} 428 \\ \times\ 2 \\ \hline \end{array} \qquad \begin{array}{r} 579 \\ \times\ 3 \\ \hline \end{array} \qquad \begin{array}{r} 920 \\ \times\ 5 \\ \hline \end{array} \qquad \begin{array}{r} 327 \\ \times\ 7 \\ \hline \end{array} \qquad \begin{array}{r} 206 \\ \times\ 3 \\ \hline \end{array} \qquad \begin{array}{r} 713 \\ \times\ 6 \\ \hline \end{array}$$

4
$$\begin{array}{r} 179 \\ \times\ 4 \\ \hline \end{array} \qquad \begin{array}{r} 803 \\ \times\ 1 \\ \hline \end{array} \qquad \begin{array}{r} 263 \\ \times\ 3 \\ \hline \end{array} \qquad \begin{array}{r} 3917 \\ \times\ 5 \\ \hline \end{array} \qquad \begin{array}{r} 5782 \\ \times\ 6 \\ \hline \end{array} \qquad \begin{array}{r} 1429 \\ \times\ 5 \\ \hline \end{array}$$

5 At Pancho's Restaurant, 310 burritos are sold each year. Pancho's has been open for 5 years. How many burritos have been sold since Pancho's opened?

$$\begin{array}{r} 310 \\ \times\ 5 \\ \hline \end{array}$$

6 Plane tickets from Miami, Florida, to Denver, Colorado, cost $522 each. The 4 members of the Wilson family are buying tickets from Miami to Denver. How much will the tickets cost? _____

7 Megan bought 5 large bags of peanuts. There are 210 peanuts in each bag. How many peanuts does she have in all? _____

Multiplication

44

⭐ When you multiply large numbers by a 2-digit number, take it step by step.

$$\begin{array}{r} 342 \\ \times\ 14 \end{array}$$

First, multiply each digit of the top number by the ones digit in the bottom number.

$$\begin{array}{r} {\scriptstyle 1} \\ 342 \\ \times\ 14 \\ \hline 1368 \end{array}$$

Now, place a 0 in the ones place. Then, multiply by the tens digit in the bottom number.

$$\begin{array}{r} 342 \\ \times\ 14 \\ \hline 1{,}368 \\ 3420 \end{array}$$

Finally, add the products.

$$\begin{array}{r} 342 \\ \times\ 14 \\ \hline 1368 \\ +3420 \\ \hline 4788 \end{array}$$

Solve.

①

| $\begin{array}{r}52\\ \times23\end{array}$ | $\begin{array}{r}36\\ \times71\end{array}$ | $\begin{array}{r}42\\ \times18\end{array}$ | $\begin{array}{r}90\\ \times36\end{array}$ | $\begin{array}{r}83\\ \times25\end{array}$ | $\begin{array}{r}74\\ \times64\end{array}$ |

②

| $\begin{array}{r}523\\ \times\ 92\end{array}$ | $\begin{array}{r}904\\ \times\ 73\end{array}$ | $\begin{array}{r}742\\ \times\ 31\end{array}$ | $\begin{array}{r}7105\\ \times\ \ 64\end{array}$ | $\begin{array}{r}1845\\ \times\ \ 13\end{array}$ | $\begin{array}{r}2749\\ \times\ \ 22\end{array}$ |

③ The innkeepers bought 12 new beds for their hotel. Each bed cost $423. How much did they spend on beds? _____

④ An overnight stay in a room at the hotel costs $105. If 47 rooms were occupied on Thursday night, how much did the innkeepers collect from guests for Thursday? _____

Multiplication

45

$\star$ When you multiply large numbers by a 3-digit number, take one step at a time.

$$\begin{array}{r} 409 \\ \times 436 \\ \hline \end{array}$$

First, multiply each digit of the top number by the ones digit in the bottom number.

$$\begin{array}{r} ^5\ 409 \\ \times\ 436 \\ \hline 2454 \end{array}$$

$$\begin{array}{r} ^2 \\ 409 \\ \times\ 436 \\ \hline 2454 \end{array}$$

Place a 0 in the ones place. Then, multiply by the tens digit in the bottom number. **1227**0

Place a 0 in the ones and tens places. Then, multiply by the hundreds digit in the bottom number.

$$\begin{array}{r} ^3 \\ 409 \\ \times\ 436 \\ \hline 2454 \\ 12270 \\ \textbf{163600} \end{array}$$

Finally, add the products. Regroup, if needed.

$$\begin{array}{r} 409 \\ \times\ 436 \\ \hline ^{11} \\ 2454 \\ 12270 \\ +163600 \\ \hline 178,324 \end{array}$$

Solve.

1

| $\begin{array}{r}324\\ \times215\end{array}$ | $\begin{array}{r}294\\ \times170\end{array}$ | $\begin{array}{r}472\\ \times358\end{array}$ | $\begin{array}{r}613\\ \times230\end{array}$ | $\begin{array}{r}195\\ \times466\end{array}$ | $\begin{array}{r}609\\ \times354\end{array}$ |

2

| $\begin{array}{r}182\\ \times375\end{array}$ | $\begin{array}{r}572\\ \times523\end{array}$ | $\begin{array}{r}493\\ \times206\end{array}$ | $\begin{array}{r}845\\ \times532\end{array}$ | $\begin{array}{r}730\\ \times656\end{array}$ | $\begin{array}{r}931\\ \times438\end{array}$ |

3 The innkeepers charge $120 for a room. If they filled 320 rooms last month, how much did they make? _____

Multiplication Practice

46

Solve.

1)

73	57	572	46	698	506
× 3	× 9	× 38	×22	× 14	× 59

2)

311	657	194	320	293	577
× 22	× 13	× 27	× 12	× 40	× 8

3)

293	927	523	702	294	827
× 38	×301	× 77	×139	×576	×865

4) Pablo loves to ride his bike. For the past 12 months, he has ridden 135 miles each month. How many miles has he ridden in the past 12 months?

_____

5) Pablo joined a biking club. There are 452 people in the club. If each person rides 135 miles each month, how many miles does the entire club ride in a month?

_____

Name _____

Division

47

⭐ When you divide large numbers by a 1-digit number, check to see if the divisor can divide the front end digit of the dividend. Place the quotient above the dividend. Subtract.

$$
\begin{array}{r} 2 \\ 4\overline{)92} \\ -8 \\ \hline 1 \end{array}
\qquad
\begin{array}{r} 23 \\ 4\overline{)92} \\ -8 \\ \hline 12 \\ -12 \\ \hline 0 \end{array}
$$

Bring down the ones digit, then divide again.

Solve.

1 $2\overline{)48}$ $3\overline{)45}$ $6\overline{)78}$ $9\overline{)99}$ $1\overline{)87}$ $5\overline{)85}$

2 $2\overline{)56}$ $8\overline{)96}$ $4\overline{)52}$ $7\overline{)91}$ $6\overline{)90}$ $9\overline{)90}$

3 $8\overline{)88}$ $5\overline{)70}$ $2\overline{)72}$ $3\overline{)75}$ $1\overline{)261}$ $6\overline{)684}$

4 The O'Connors paid $78 for water park tickets. There are 6 people in the family. How much was each ticket? _____

Division

48

⭐ If you cannot divide the first digit of the dividend by the divisor, see if the divisor can divide the first two digits of the dividend. Place the quotient above the dividend. Subtract.

$$\begin{array}{r} 7 \\ 9\overline{)675} \\ -63 \\ \hline 4 \end{array} \qquad \begin{array}{r} 75 \\ 9\overline{)675} \\ -63 \\ \hline 45 \\ -45 \\ \hline 0 \end{array}$$

Bring down the ones digit, then divide again.

Solve.

1 $7\overline{)91}$ $6\overline{)84}$ $3\overline{)48}$ $1\overline{)79}$ $6\overline{)96}$ $5\overline{)150}$

2 $2\overline{)56}$ $8\overline{)272}$ $5\overline{)215}$ $7\overline{)623}$ $7\overline{)168}$ $9\overline{)207}$

3 $8\overline{)368}$ $3\overline{)333}$ $4\overline{)924}$ $2\overline{)156}$ $9\overline{)270}$ $4\overline{)96}$

Name _____

49

⭐ Remember to add 0 as a placeholder if needed.

```
      420
  3)1260
   -12
     06
     -6
     00
     - 0
      0
```

Solve.

1   3)906   3)924   8)984   5)1600   7)1617   4)1368

2   8)1096   3)1803   1)2937   2)1508   9)2187   5)1710

3   4)3004   6)2748   9)3123   7)4767   2)740   6)744

Division Practice

50

Solve.

1. $6\overline{)72}$ $8\overline{)88}$ $3\overline{)45}$ $4\overline{)64}$ $5\overline{)75}$ $7\overline{)84}$

2. $2\overline{)328}$ $5\overline{)525}$ $8\overline{)600}$ $9\overline{)378}$ $7\overline{)315}$ $6\overline{)498}$

3. $4\overline{)2964}$ $5\overline{)490}$ $9\overline{)1233}$ $6\overline{)4446}$ $3\overline{)1410}$ $2\overline{)1712}$

4. Jenny has 176 books. If the bookcase has 8 shelves, how many books can she put on each shelf?

    _____

Problem Solving

51

⭐ Mom's plates have 5 flowers on each one. If there are 6 plates, how many flowers are there altogether? 5 x 6 = 30 There are 30 flowers.

Mom has 24 cherries. If there are 4 people, how many cherries will each person get? 24 ÷ 4 = 6 Each person will get 6 cherries.

Decide which operation to use. Solve.

1 Jessie organized her family's CDs into racks that hold 9 CDs. If the family has 72 CDs, how many racks does Jessie need? _____

2 Amber keeps her baseball cards in a special book. Each page holds 8 cards each. If Amber has 35 pages, how many cards can she keep in the book? _____

3 Ryan and his dad made muffins. They needed to make 24 muffins. Only 6 muffins fit on a muffin tray. How many trays will they need? _____

4 Ryan found a muffin tray that holds 12 muffins. If they use the tray 2 times, how many muffins can they make? _____

5 Ryan made 24 muffins for his slumber party. If there are 8 boys, how many muffins could each boy eat? _____

6 Molly earns $21 a day working at the juice shop. If she worked 4 days last week, how much money did she make? _____

7 There are 52 kids at camp. The kids are staying in 4 large cabins. How many kids will be in each cabin? _____

Name _____

Problem Solving

52

⭐ Some story problems have two steps. Paul had 10 T-shirts in his closet on Wednesday. On Thursday, he washed his clothes and put 3 more clean T-shirts in the closet.

On Friday, Paul packed 7 T-shirts to go to visit his grandmother. How many T-shirts does Paul have in his closet now?

First, figure out how many T-shirts Paul had on Thursday. $10 + 3 = 13$.
Then, figure out how many T-shirts he had on Friday. $13 - 7 = 6$.
There are 6 T-shirts left in Paul's closet.

Solve. Label your answers.

1. Mike made baggies of trail mix for his family. First, he made a batch of 10 baggies of trail mix, then he made a batch of 20 baggies. He wants to divide the baggies equally between his 5 family members. How many baggies of trail mix should he give to each family member?
   Step 1 _____
   Step 2 _____

2. KayLee bought 5 bags of beads at the bead store. Each bag has 8 beads. If KayLee wants to make 4 necklaces with an equal number of beads on each necklace, how many beads should she put on each necklace?
   Step 1 _____
   Step 2 _____

3. Becky and her mom are going on a trip. Yesterday, they left home and drove 108.3 miles. Today, they drove 56.7 miles before they realized that Becky forgot her sweater at a gas station. If they had to back track 8.6 miles to the gas station, how far are they from home (while at the gas station)?
   Step 1 _____
   Step 2 _____

4. Cody had $\frac{11}{12}$ of a bag of pretzels in the cupboard. He ate $\frac{7}{12}$ of the bag. Then, he found $\frac{5}{12}$ of a bag of pretzels in the pantry. How many bags of pretzels does he have in all?
   Step 1 _____
   Step 2 _____

5. Trevor had 76 marbles in his collection. Then, he received 12 more for his birthday. If he separates the marbles into 4 boxes, how many marbles will be in each box?
   Step 1 _____
   Step 2 _____

Mixed Practice

53

Solve.

1
$$\begin{array}{r} 47 \\ \times\ 3 \\ \hline \end{array}$$
$6\overline{)72}$
$$\begin{array}{r} 26.37 \\ +\ 3.9 \\ \hline \end{array}$$
$$\begin{array}{r} 29 \\ \times 61 \\ \hline \end{array}$$
$2\overline{)58}$
$7\overline{)105}$

2
$$\begin{array}{r} 40 \\ \times 63 \\ \hline \end{array}$$
$$\begin{array}{r} 34 \\ \times 25 \\ \hline \end{array}$$
$8\overline{)168}$
$7\overline{)322}$
$$\begin{array}{r} 5763 \\ -3294 \\ \hline \end{array}$$
$$\begin{array}{r} 37.09 \\ -34.5 \\ \hline \end{array}$$

3
$5\overline{)370}$
$$\begin{array}{r} 55 \\ \times 23 \\ \hline \end{array}$$
$$\begin{array}{r} 146 \\ \times\ 13 \\ \hline \end{array}$$
$$\begin{array}{r} 453 \\ \times\ 84 \\ \hline \end{array}$$
$$\begin{array}{r} 351 \\ +873 \\ \hline \end{array}$$
$5\overline{)3415}$

4
$9\overline{)7038}$
$$\begin{array}{r} 746 \\ \times 209 \\ \hline \end{array}$$
$4\overline{)1388}$
$$\begin{array}{r} 287 \\ \times\ 32 \\ \hline \end{array}$$
$$\begin{array}{r} 2974 \\ +1098 \\ \hline \end{array}$$
$$\begin{array}{r} 472 \\ \times 965 \\ \hline \end{array}$$

5 The band called the Screamers is playing in town for the next 4 nights. There are 42 seats in the club and all 4 shows are sold out. How many tickets were sold in all?

_____

6 Billy, Marta, and Tom just won $72. If they split the money evenly, how many dollars will each friend have?

_____

Mixed Practice

54

Solve.

1. Maria bought 5 pairs of pants for $21 each. How much did she spend on pants? _____

2. It's a 675-mile drive to San Francisco. Four people will be taking the trip. If they split the driving equally, how much will each person have to drive? How many extra miles will one person have to drive? _____

3. The Corner Store just received a shipment of 4 boxes of energy bars. If each box holds 128 energy bars, how many are there to sell? _____

4. The fish tank needs 65 gallons of water. Grace filled the tank using a 5-gallon bucket. How many times did Grace have to fill her bucket in order to fill the tank? _____

5. Hailey read 3 books this month. If she read 3 books that are all about 230 pages long, how many pages did she read? _____

6. Eight teammates biked equal distances in a relay race. If they biked 104 miles total, how many miles did each team member bike? _____

7. Caleb compared prices at different music stores. At the Music Palace, the CD he wants costs $14.97. At Music Music, it costs $16.50. How much will he save if he buys the CD at the Music Palace? _____

8. Shanique and Rachael combined their bead collections. If Shanique had $\frac{1}{2}$ of a jar of beads and Rachael had $\frac{5}{6}$ of a jar of beads, how many jars of beads do they have together? _____

Name _____

Take a Test Drive

Test-Taking Tip: If you are stuck on a problem, come back to it after you finish the rest of the problems.

Fill in the bubble beside the correct answer.

1

56
+32

- ○ 24
- ○ 84
- ○ 88
- ○ 98

---

5 The weight limit for suitcases on the airplane is 45.5 pounds. Seth's suitcase weighed 67.3 pounds. How many pounds does Seth have to leave at home so that his suitcase will be allowed on the plane?

- ○ 22.2 pounds
- ○ 20.7 pounds
- ○ 21.8 pounds
- ○ 22.8 pounds

---

2 $\dfrac{17}{18} - \dfrac{13}{18} =$

- ○ $\dfrac{1}{6}$
- ○ $\dfrac{1}{3}$
- ○ $\dfrac{2}{8}$
- ○ $\dfrac{2}{9}$

6

8.25
+7.8

- ○ 16.05
- ○ 16.33
- ○ 16.5
- ○ 15.95

---

3 $\dfrac{8}{12} + \dfrac{10}{12} =$

- ○ $1\dfrac{5}{12}$
- ○ $1\dfrac{1}{2}$
- ○ $\dfrac{1}{6}$
- ○ $1\dfrac{3}{4}$

---

7 Which equation shows the Distributive Property of multiplication?

- ○ 9 (8 + 3) = 98 + 93
- ○ 9 (8 + 3) = (9 x 8) + (9 x 3)
- ○ 9 (8 + 3) = 9 x 8 x 3
- ○ 9 (8 + 3) = (9 x 8) + (8 x 3)

4

7.88
−4.59

- ○ 3.31
- ○ 12.47
- ○ 3.29
- ○ 12.3

---

8 $\dfrac{7}{8} - \dfrac{1}{4}$

- ○ $\dfrac{6}{4}$
- ○ $\dfrac{5}{8}$
- ○ $1\dfrac{1}{4}$
- ○ $1\dfrac{1}{2}$

Name _____

Take a Test Drive

Fill in the bubble beside the correct answer.

1
17
× 5

○ 35
○ 55
○ 65
○ 85

5 8)184

○ 23
○ 33
○ 120
○ 123

2 3)78

○ 16
○ 26
○ 222
○ 260

6 4)3108

○ 77
○ 127
○ 707
○ 777

3
725
× 93

○ 8700
○ 66,015
○ 67,425
○ 70,725

7
907
× 6

○ 5402
○ 5442
○ 5462
○ 5642

4 The total cost for a new television set is $248. Four friends split the cost and shared the television. How much did each friend spend?

○ $62
○ $82
○ $81
○ $63

8
218
× 42

○ 1308
○ 8846
○ 9156
○ 9166

Length

57

⭐ We use inches, feet, and yards to measure length.

1 yard (yd) = 3 feet (ft)
1 foot = 12 inches (in.)

The ruler shows how inches are usually divided.

How long is this pencil? $3\frac{3}{4}$ inches

Use the ruler to answer the question.

1 How long is the eraser?

_____

2 How long is the car?

_____

3 How long is the worm?

_____

4 How long is the paper clip?

_____

5 Matt is 60 inches tall. What is his height in feet? _____

Name _____

58

★ The **perimeter** of a shape is the distance around it.

To find perimeter, add the length of all of its sides. $P = 4 + 6 + 9 + 3 + 7 = 29$ inches

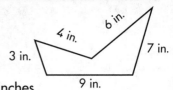

Find the perimeter.

1   [rectangle: 7 in., 10 in.]

Perimeter = _____

2   [square: 7 yd, 7 yd, 7 yd, 7 yd]

Perimeter = _____

3   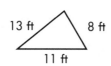 [triangle: 13 ft, 8 ft, 11 ft]

Perimeter = _____

4   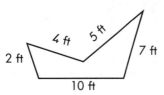 [shape: 2 ft, 4 ft, 5 ft, 7 ft, 10 ft]

Perimeter = _____

5   [square: 6 ft, 6 ft]

Perimeter = _____

6   [rectangle: 3 in., 8 in.]

Perimeter = _____

7   Franco put up a new fence around his yard. How much fencing did he need? _____

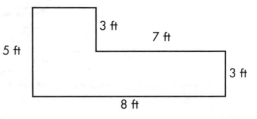
[L-shaped figure: 4 ft, 3 ft, 7 ft, 5 ft, 3 ft, 8 ft]

8   Mrs. Jones sewed an edge onto a rectangular table cloth. One of the sides is 20 inches long and another is 30 inches long. How many inches of edging material did she need? _____

Area

59

⭐ **Area** is all the space covered by a shape.

To find the area, multiply the length by the width.

Length = 8
Width = 6
Area = $L \times W = 8 \times 6 = 48$ square inches (sq in.)
Count the squares to check the answer.

8 in.

6 in.

Find the area.

1 9 in.

5 in.

Area = _____

12 in.

8 in.

Area = _____

2 9 in.

3 in.

Area of the shaded region = _____

10 in.

5 in.

Area of the shaded region = _____

3 7 ft

4 ft

Area = _____

6 in.

6 in.

Area = _____

Draw a picture to help you answer the questions. Remember to label your drawings.

4 Meg painted one side of the fence in her yard. If the fence is 5 feet high by 12 feet long, what is the area of the fence?

_____

5 Rishi got rolls of grass to cover his yard. The yard is 16 feet by 9 feet. Find the area of his yard to determine how much grass he needed. _____

Name _____

Volume

60

⭐ **Volume** is the amount of space inside a shape.

To find the volume, multiply the length by the width by the height.

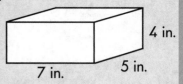

Volume = L x W x H = 4 x 5 x 7 = 140 cubic inches

Find the volume. Label your answer.

1

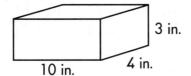

10 in.   4 in.   3 in.

Volume = _____

8 ft   6 ft   5 ft

Volume = _____

2

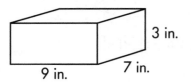

9 in.   7 in.   3 in.

Volume = _____

8 ft   8 ft   4 ft

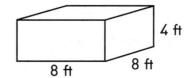

Volume = _____

---

3 Gabriel measured his refrigerator. The dimensions, or measurements, of the refrigerator are 5 feet by 2 feet by 3 feet. What is the volume? _____

4 The volume of Bianca's bathtub is 36 cubic feet. If the tub is 6 feet long and 2 feet deep, how wide is the tub? _____

5 Alexis has a paper clip holder that is 10 centimeters high, 5 centimeters wide, and 5 centimeters long. What is its volume? _____

Time

61

⭐ Time is measured in seconds, minutes, hours, and days.

60 seconds = 1 minute
60 minutes = 1 hour
24 hours = 1 day

Math class is 1 _____ long.
You wouldn't describe the length of math class in seconds or days.
Hours probably best fits this sentence.

Multiply or divide to convert the time intervals.

1 180 seconds = _____ minutes   72 hours = _____ days

2 300 minutes = _____ hours   2 days = _____ hours

3 250 seconds = _____ minutes   60 hours = _____ days and _____ hours
and _____ seconds

Write **seconds, minutes, hours,** or **days** to tell how long each activity would take.

4 walk a block _____   say the alphabet _____

5 finish a math page _____   walk 10 miles _____

6 drive across the country _____   answer the phone _____

Write **seconds, minutes, hours,** or **days** to complete the story.

On Tuesday, Jane went for a 30 _____ walk. She had to stop for
45 _____ to tie her shoe. After her walk, she spent 2 _____ on her
homework. In 4 _____, it will by Saturday. Jane hopes to spend 7 _____
on Saturday at her grandmother's house playing games and planting
flowers in her grandmother's garden.

Time

62

★ We also measure time in weeks, months, years, decades, and centuries.

7 days = 1 week
4 weeks = 1 month (a month can have 28, 29, 30, or 31 days)
12 months = 1 year (a year has 365 days)
10 years = 1 decade (the prefix **dec-** means 10)
100 years = 10 decades = 1 century (the prefix **cent-** means 100)

Three ____centuries____ ago the United States did not exist.

Multiply or divide to convert the time intervals.

1 28 days = _____ weeks   144 months = _____ years

2 40 years = _____ decades   3 months = 90 _____

3 2 centuries = 200 _____   730 days = 2 _____

Write **weeks, years,** or **centuries** to tell how long each activity would take.

4 walk from California to Utah _____   mountains wear away _____

5 trees to grow tall _____   build a house _____

6 finish the fourth grade _____   finish going to school _____

Finish the story by filling in the blanks with the correct time intervals. Write **days, weeks, months, years, decades,** or **centuries.**

Paul's family may be moving in 9 _____—just a little less than a year. Paul has lived in California for 8 _____, which is most of his life. Paul's mom says that the new town will be really interesting. The town is 2 _____ old—that's almost as old as our country! In 24 _____, Paul and his family are going to visit the new town. They will spend two _____ there looking for a new house and checking out Paul's new school. Paul is very excited!

Angles

63

⭐ An **angle** is the figure formed where two lines meet. Angles are measured in degrees. There are 360° in a full circle.

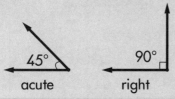 45°
acute

 90°
right

 105°
obtuse

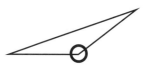 180°
straight

Circle the answer that best describes the angle.

1

| obtuse | right | | obtuse | right | | obtuse | right |
| acute | straight | | acute | straight | | acute | straight |

2

| obtuse | right | | obtuse | right | | obtuse | right |
| acute | straight | | acute | straight | | acute | straight |

3

| obtuse | right | | obtuse | right | | obtuse | right |
| acute | straight | | acute | straight | | acute | straight |

Fill in the blanks with the correct word or angle.

4 A square has 4 _____ or 90° angles.

5 This right triangle has 1 right angle and 2 _____ angles.

6 A line has a _____ or straight angle.

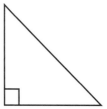

Name _____

64

⭐ This angle is called ∠ ABC.

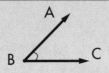

This triangle is called △ DEF.
The sum of all of the angles of a triangle is 180°.
45° + 45° + 90° = 180°
∠ DEF + ∠ EFD + ∠ FDE = 180°

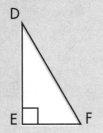

Follow the directions to answer the questions.

1

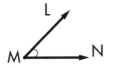

What is the name of this angle?

_____

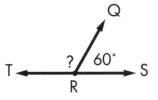

What is the measure of ∠ TRQ?

_____

2

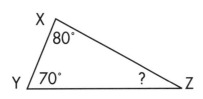

What is the measure of ∠ YZX?

_____

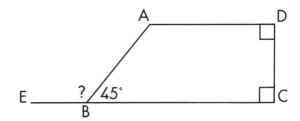

What is the measure of ∠ ABE?

_____

Draw a picture of these figures. Label the angles in degrees.

3 right triangle (a triangle with a right angle)

4 a 4-sided figure with at least 1 right angle

Name _____

Standard and Metric Measures

65

⭐ The United States uses the standard measurement system. People in other parts of the world use the metric measurement system.

	Standard	Metric
Length	miles (mi), feet (ft), inches (in.)	kilometers (km), meters (m), centimeters (cm)
Weight	pounds (lbs), ounces (oz)	kilograms (kg), grams (g)
Temperature	degrees Fahrenheit (°F)	degrees Celsius (°C)

Find the measurements. Label your answers correctly.

1 What is the temperature?

_____

How much do the apples weigh?

_____

2 What is the area of the garden?

_____

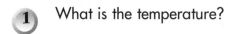
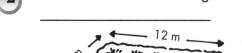

How long is the candle?

_____

3 What is the temperature?

_____

How much does the pencil weigh?

_____

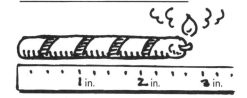

4 How much does the dog weigh?

_____

How many miles is it from Ashville to Iowa City? _____

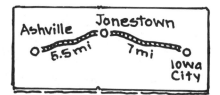

Story Problems

66

Solve.

1. Paige's metric thermometer says that the temperature outside is 21°. Justine can't remember what the metric units are called. Help her by writing the unit name on the line. 21° _____

2. Using the standard measuring system, Blake found the weight and length of his suitcase. He wrote down the measurements, but he forgot to label them. Help him by labeling the measurements. Weight: 10 _____ Length: 24 _____ or 2 _____

3. Keisha measured the couch in her living room. She found that it is 8.3 m long. On the line, write what **m** stands for and write the name of the measuring system that Keisha is using. m = _____ System = _____

4. If Mr. Nguyen found the dimensions of his garage to be 15 ft x 10 ft x 7 ft. What system of measurement was he using? What does **ft** stand for?
System = _____ ft = _____

5. Sammy knows that 180° and 90° angles have special names, but she can't remember what they are. 180° is a _____ angle. 90° is a _____ angle.

6. Using the metric system, Jake found the following measurements for the box of books. Label his measurements.
Length: 1 _____ and 17 _____
Weight: 9 _____ and 56 _____

7. Fernando's front yard is 7 m long by 5 m wide. He wants to replace the fence and reseed the lawn. Help him figure out how much fencing material and grass seed he needs by finding the perimeter and area of his yard.
Perimeter: _____ Area: _____

8. Kim dug a huge hole in her backyard to put in a pool. She wants the pool to have a volume of 540 cubic feet. The hole is already 10 ft long and 9 ft wide. How deep does it have to be in order to have the correct volume?
Depth = _____

Mixed Practice

67

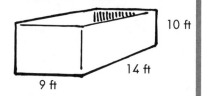

⭐ Perimeter = 14 + 9 + 14 + 9 = 46 ft
Area = 14 x 9 = 126 square feet
Volume = 14 x 9 x 10 = 1260 cubic feet

Solve.

1

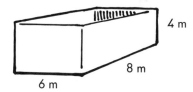

Volume = _____

Perimeter of the tabletop: _____
Area of the tabletop: _____

2

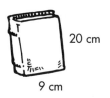

Perimeter of the front cover: _____
Area of the front cover: _____

Volume of the cabinet: _____

3 Write these time words in order from shortest to longest amount of time: centuries, days, hours, seconds, weeks, years

_____

Draw a line to match the angle with its name and degrees.

4   straight   45°

5   right   90°

6   obtuse   105°

7   acute   180°

Name _____

Tables and Charts

68

⭐ Different tables and charts help us organize time.

Use the calendar to answer the questions.

1 What day of the week is August 14th? _____

2 What is the date of the first Monday of August? _____

3 If Jada spent 2 weeks at her aunt and uncle's house and she left on August 7th, what day did she get back? _____

4 Mr. Liu will be out of town for most of August. If he leaves on the first Friday of August and comes back on the last Friday, how many days will he be gone?
_____

Answer the questions using the bus schedule.

New York–Washington, D.C., Bus Schedule

	Departure from New York	Arrival in Washington	Departure from Washington	Arrival in New York
Sunday	8:30 A.M.	11:30 A.M.	1:45 P.M.	4:45 P.M.
Monday	7:15 A.M.	10:15 A.M.	3:30 P.M.	6:30 P.M.
Tuesday	7:15 A.M.	10:15 A.M.	3:30 P.M.	6:30 P.M.
Wednesday	7:15 A.M.	10:15 A.M.	3:30 P.M.	6:30 P.M.
Thursday	7:15 A.M.	10:15 A.M.	3:30 P.M.	6:30 P.M.
Friday	7:15 A.M.	10:15 A.M.	3:30 P.M.	6:30 P.M.
Saturday	8:30 A.M.	11:30 A.M.	1:45 P.M.	4:45 P.M.

5 How long is the trip from New York to Washington, D.C.? _____

6 Alejandro left from New York for Washington, D.C., on Monday and returned from Washington to New York on Saturday. What time did he leave New York and what time did he return?
Left: _____   Returned: _____

7 Mandy traveled from Washington, D.C., to New York. If she left before 2:00 P.M., on which days could she have traveled? _____

8 Jon scheduled a meeting in Washington, D.C., on Tuesday at 10:00 A.M. If he left New York on the morning bus, did he make it to his meeting on time? _____

Take a Test Drive

Test-Taking Tip: Pay attention to the labels in each answer choice. They give units of length, weight, temperature, angle measurement, and time.

Fill in the bubble beside the correct answer.

1 How long is the piece of gum?

- ○ $1\frac{1}{2}$ oz
- ○ $1\frac{3}{4}$ in.
- ○ $1\frac{1}{2}$ in.
- ○ 1.5 cm

5 240 seconds = 4 _____
- ○ nanoseconds
- ○ minutes
- ○ hours
- ○ days

2 What is the perimeter of the front of the television set?

12 cm

18 cm

- ○ 60 cm
- ○ 30 in.
- ○ 30 cm
- ○ 22 m

6 _____ years = 1095 days
- ○ 3
- ○ 10
- ○ 4
- ○ 1

3 What is the area of the top of the bed?

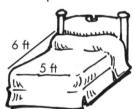

6 ft

5 ft

- ○ 11 ft
- ○ 30 sq ft
- ○ 30 ft
- ○ 22 sq ft

7 How many right angles does this figure have?

- ○ 5
- ○ 4
- ○ 2
- ○ 3

4 What is the volume of the milk carton?

9 cm

8 cm   5 cm

- ○ 360 sq cm
- ○ 320 cm
- ○ 360 cu cm
- ○ 36 cm

8 ∠ KMN measures ___

K

L   45°   N

M

- ○ 180°
- ○ 135°
- ○ 45°
- ○ 90°C

Name _____

Take a Test Drive

Fill in the bubble beside the correct answer.

---

1 ∠ CAB is ___

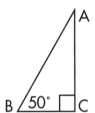

- ○ 40°
- ○ 60°
- ○ 30°
- ○ 90°

---

2 The baby weighs 35 _____.

- ○ m
- ○ lbs
- ○ cm
- ○ ft

---

3 It's an obtuse angle because it's _____ 90°.

- ○ <
- ○ =
- ○ >
- ○ > and =

---

4 Lauren measured the bookcase with a ruler. Which of the follow could NOT be the measurement of the bookcase?

- ○ 36 in.
- ○ 36 cm
- ○ 3.6 ft
- ○ 36 oz

---

5 It's really hot outside. It must be at least 95 ___.

- ○ °
- ○ °F
- ○ C
- ○ °CF

---

6 What is the area of the book?

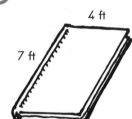

- ○ 14 sq ft
- ○ 28 sq ft
- ○ 14 cu ft
- ○ 28 cu ft

---

7 The volume of the cooler is 12 cubic feet. What could the dimensions be?

- ○ 12 ft by 1 ft by 2 ft
- ○ 6 ft by 4 ft by 2 ft
- ○ 2 ft by 3 ft by 2 ft
- ○ 3 ft by 4 ft

---

8 Sabrina has piano lessons every Tuesday. How many lessons will she have in June?

- ○ 10
- ○ 5
- ○ 4
- ○ 30

Name _____

Dimensions

⭐ Two- and three-dimensional figures have many different properties. A line has one dimension: length.

6 | This circle has two dimensions: width and length. The diameter of a circle is the same as its width. *d* = 6

6

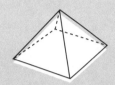

This figure has three dimensions: width, length, and height.
Number of faces or sides = 5
Number of edges = 8
Number of vertices or points = 5

Fill in the missing information.

1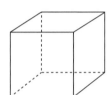

Number of dimensions = _____
Number of faces or sides = _____
Number of edges = _____
Number of vertices (points) = _____

2

Number of dimensions = _____
Width = 15, D = _____

3

5 = Number of _____
6 = Number of _____
3 = Number of _____

Draw the following figures.

4 A one-dimensional figure

5 A two-dimensional figure that is not a circle

6 A three-dimensional figure

Dimensions

72

Two-Dimensional Shapes		
Prefix	**Meaning**	**Shape**
Tri-	3	Triangle
Quad-	4	Rectangle or Square
Pent-	5	Pentagon
Hex-	6	Hexagon
Hept-	7	Heptagon
Oct-	8	Octagon
Poly-	Many	anything with 3 or more sides

Draw the figure named.

 Triangle   Hexagon   Polygon

Write the name below each figure.

            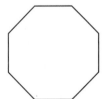   

_____   _____   _____

Brainstorm.

 Write as many other words you know that have the same prefixes (such as **tripod**).

_____   _____   _____

_____   _____   _____

_____   _____   _____

_____   _____   _____

Similar Figures

73

⭐ **Similar figures** have the same exact shape. They do not have to be the same size.

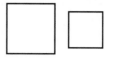

similar   not similar

Write **similar** or **not similar**.

1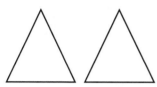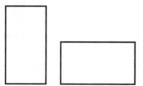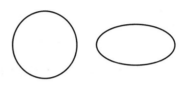

_____   _____   _____

2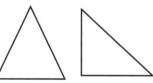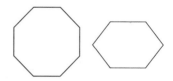

_____   _____   _____

Draw the following figures.

3 Two quadrilaterals that are NOT similar

4 Two pentagons that are similar but not the same size

5 A three-dimensional figure

Congruent Figures

74

⭐ **Congruent figures** are exactly the same shape and size.

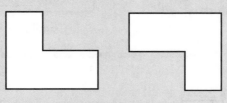

CONGRUENT   NOT CONGRUENT

Write **congruent** or **not congruent.**

1

_____   _____   _____

2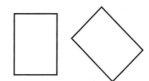

_____   _____   _____

Draw a congruent figure to match the figure shown.

3

4

Geometric Figures

75

⭐ When you flip a figure, you show its mirror image.

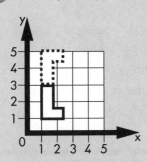

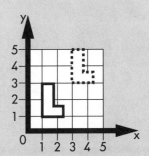

This is called a **flip.** To draw a flipped figure, imagine that you are picking the figure up and flipping it over.

This is a **slide.** To slide a figure, you just move it in any direction. The L was moved up and to the right.

Flip the figure.

 1

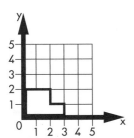 **2**

Slide the figure.

 3

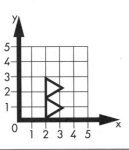

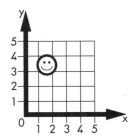

Geometric Figures

76

 Turning an image changes its position.

90° clockwise   180°

Clockwise means in the direction hands on a clock move.
Counterclockwise means the opposite direction of a clock's hands.
0°—no change
180°—the same as a flip

Circle the answer.

1

0°
90° counterclockwise
90° clockwise
180°

0°
90° counterclockwise
90° clockwise
180°

2

0°
90° counterclockwise
90° clockwise
180°

0°
90° counterclockwise
90° clockwise
180°

3

0°
90° counterclockwise
90° clockwise
180°

Draw any figure. Then draw
the same shape flipped 180°.

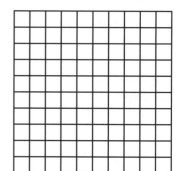

Name _____

Graphing

77

⭐ A pair of coordinates gives an exact location on a graph. The line across the bottom is the *x*-axis. The line up the left side is the *y*-axis.

To find the coordinates for A, go across 3, then up 1. Coordinates are written (*x*, *y*) or (3, 1) for A.

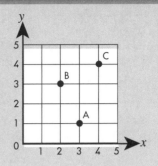

Write the coordinates. Use the graph above.

1 What are the coordinates for B? _____   What are the coordinates for C? _____

Use the following graph for problems 2 and 3.

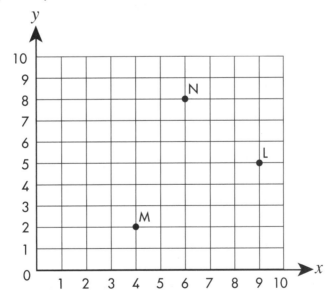

2 What are the coordinates for N? _____

What is the *x*-axis coordinate for M (how far across do you go)? _____

3 What is the *y*-axis coordinate for L (how far up do you go)? _____

If you move M 2 units to the right and 3 units up, where would it be? _____

Name _____

78

⭐ When you plot points or draw them on a graph, the first number is on the *x*-axis (across) and the second number is on the *y*-axis (up).

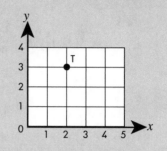

Point T is at (2, 3).

Plot the coordinates above.

1   Plot E (4, 1)   Plot F (4, 2)   Plot C (3, 2)

2   Plot G (1, 2)   Plot H (0, 4)   Plot B (5, 0)

Plot the new coordinates.

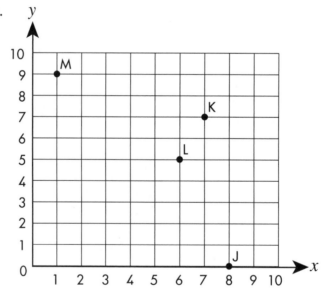

3   Move J 1 unit to the right and 4 up. Label the new coordinate R.

Move K 3 units to the left and 2 up. Label the new coordinate S.

4   Move L 6 units to the left and 5 down. Label the new coordinate V.

Move M 8 units to the right and 1 unit down. Label the new coordinate W.

Name _____

Story Problems

79

Solve.

1. Alejandro put new carpet in his living room. The room is 9 m long and 5 m wide. How many square meters of carpeting will he need? _____

2. Monique put her favorite picture in a frame. The picture is 18 in. wide by 24 in. long. How many inches of framing material will she need? _____

3. The dimensions of the new garage are 30 m long by 9 m wide. What is the area of the new garage? _____

4. Mr. and Mrs. Williams took their dog for a walk around the block. Their block is 75 m long on the south and north sides and 90 m long on the east and west sides. How long was their walk? _____

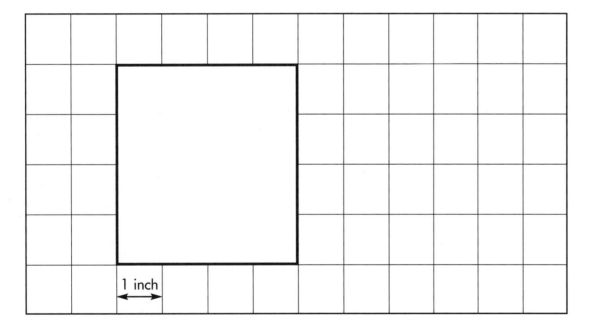

1 inch

5. What is the perimeter and area of the figure? Hint: Count each square as 1 unit.
   Perimeter: _____   Area: _____

6. What are the coordinates for each corner of the figure above?
   bottom left: _____ bottom right: _____
   top left: _____ top right: _____

Name _____

Story Problems

80

Solve.

1 Alicia built a shed in the backyard. Each of the four walls is 7 ft by 8 ft. How much wood did she use for the four walls? _____

2 Coach Hensley asked the team to run 3 laps around the football field. If the field is 100 yd long by 50 yd wide, how far will the team run? _____

3 Dave and Kim are putting in a new tile floor in their bathroom. The tiles cost $3 per square foot. If the bathroom is 9 ft long by 10 ft wide, how much will they be spending on tile? _____

4 Ori has decided to paint the front of the house. One liter of paint covers 4 square meters. The dimensions of the front of the house are 12 m long by 9 m high. How many liters of paint will he need? _____

Draw the figure on the graph. Then solve the problem.

5 Ms. Kellar is planning to put ribbon around the edge of her pillows. Each pillow is square with 8-inch sides. If she wants to decorate 6 pillows, how much ribbon will she need?

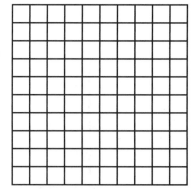

6 The contractor said that it will cost $8 per square meter to replace the carpeting in Shawn's house. If the room that he wants to carpet is 9 m long by 9 m wide, and Shawn has only $600 to spend on the project, how much more money does he need to pay for the carpeting?

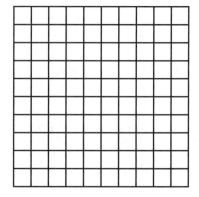

Name _____

Take a Test Drive

Test-Taking Tip: Study the drawings and their labels carefully before you answer questions about them.

Fill in the bubble beside the correct answer.

1 How many vertices does this cube have?
- ○ 8
- ○ 6
- ○ 11
- ○ 3

2 What is the diameter of this circle?

10 cm

10 cm
- ○ 20 cm
- ○ 100 sq. cm
- ○ 10 cm
- ○ 5 cm

3 This figure is called a(n) _____.
- ○ hexilateral
- ○ heptagon
- ○ octagon
- ○ hexagon

4 How many sides does a pentagon have?
- ○ 4
- ○ 5
- ○ 6
- ○ 7

5 Which 2 figures are similar?
- ○
- ○
- ○
- ○

6 Which figure is congruent to N?

N
- ○
- ○
- ○
- ○

7 What is 25 rounded to the nearest 10?
- ○ 20
- ○ 26
- ○ 30
- ○ 40

8 Which pair of figures is congruent?
- ○
- ○
- ○
- ○

Name _____

Take a Test Drive

Fill in the bubble beside the correct answer.

---

1 These figures are
_____.

- ○ congruent
- ○ flipped images
- ○ similar
- ○ turned images

4 What are the coordinates for E?

- ○ (1, 5)
- ○ (2, 2)
- ○ (0, 4)
- ○ (4, 0)

---

2 This figure has been turned _____.

- ○ 0°
- ○ 90° counter-clockwise
- ○ 90° clockwise
- ○ 180°

5 Which point is at (5, 1)?

- ○ A
- ○ B
- ○ C
- ○ D

---

3 This figure has been turned _____.

- ○ 0°
- ○ 90° counter-clockwise
- ○ 90° clockwise
- ○ 180°

6 If C is moved 2 units to the right and 2 units down, what will be its new coordinates?

- ○ (1, 5)
- ○ (3, 5)
- ○ (3, 3)
- ○ (1, 3)

Use the graph for items 4–6.

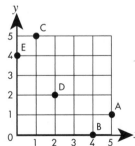

7 The perimeter of the playground is 160 ft. If the playground is 35 ft long, how wide is it?

- ○ 35 ft
- ○ 45 m
- ○ 90 ft
- ○ 45 ft

Mathematical Relationships

83

⭐ Recognizing how numbers relate to each other will help you find patterns.

3, 7, 10, 14, 17, 21, . . .
Pattern: $^+4$, $^+3$, $^+4$, $^+3$, $^+4$, . . .
The next number will be 21 + 3 = 24

Complete the pattern.

1 2, 5, 7, 10, 12, 15, . . .
Pattern: _____
Next number: _____

1, 2, 4, 7, 11, 16, . . .
Pattern: _____
Next number: _____

2 1, 2, 4, 8, 16, 32, . . .
Pattern: _____
Next number: _____

100, 99, 97, 94, 90, 85, 79, . . .
Pattern: _____
Next number: _____

3 _____, 6, 11, 12, 17, 18, 23, 24, . . .
Pattern: _____
First number: _____

_____, 4, 9, 16, 25, 36, 49, . . .
Pattern: _____
First number: _____

4 _____
Pattern: count by 100s
First number: 201

_____
Pattern: $^-2$, $^+5$, $^-1$, $^-2$, $^+5$, $^-1$
First number: 50

5 Create your own number pattern. Have someone else guess the pattern.
Pattern: _____

_____

Rule: _____

_____

_____

Name _____

Tables and Charts

84

⭐ What is missing in this chart?
When you input a number, the output is
that number times 8. Test this idea. Does
2 x 8 = 16? Does 9 x 8 = 72?
Does 5 x 8 = 40? (Yes)
Pattern: Input x 8 = Output
64 ÷ 8 = 8, which is the missing number.

Input	Output
2	16
9	72
?	64
5	40

Identify the pattern and complete the chart.

 1

Input	Output
54	9
_____	4
6	1
36	6
60	_____
12	2

Pattern: _____

Initial	Final
6	11
10	15
3	_____
8	13
_____	26

Pattern: _____

 2

Entered	Received
☐	△
⬡	_____
⬠	☐
_____	⬡

Pattern: _____

Input	Output
9	81
1	_____
6	36
4	16
2	4
_____	49

Pattern: _____

Variables

85

⭐ A variable is a letter that represents an unknown number.

Seven times a number is $7 \times n = 7n$
Use n to represent the unknown number.

Eight plus a number is $8 + n$
You can use variables with all operations.

Write the number sentence using a variable.

1 Fifteen minus a number _____   Fifty divided by a number _____

2 Twelve times a number _____   A number plus twenty-one _____

3 A number minus three _____   A number divided by 8 _____

4 Eight times a number _____   A number times three hundred _____

5 Eleven plus a number minus thirteen   A number times nine divided by five

_____   _____

Create number sentences for these problems using variables.

6 Patty has 2 buckets of apples. There are 15 apples in one bucket and an unknown number in the other. Write a number sentence to show how many apples she has. _____

7 Dominic had 14 marbles. Then he lost an unknown number of marbles. Write a number sentence to show how many marbles there are now.

_____

Variables

86

⭐ Using variables, you can set up an equation for a problem.

Aaron bought 12 flowers for Sheila on Thursday and an unknown number of flowers for her on Friday. If Sheila has 18 flowers in all, how many flowers did Aaron buy for her on Friday?
Set up: $12 + n = 18$

Angelica spent $2 on juice and $3 for a sandwich. How much did she spend in all? $\$2 + \$3 = x$

Using a variable to represent the unknown number, set up an equation for the problem. Then solve the problem.

1 At the track meet, there were 21 events in the morning and an unknown number of events in the afternoon. Throughout the entire day, there were 34 events in all. How many events were there in the afternoon?
Set up: _____
Solution: _____

2 Dakota had $13 in his pocket this morning. He spent an unknown amount of money on lunch. When he got home in the afternoon, he had $9 in his pocket. How much money did he spend on lunch?
Set up: _____
Solution: _____

3 Noah divided his collection of 450 pennies into an unknown number of bags. If there are 45 pennies in each bag, how many bags did Noah use?
Set up: _____
Solution: _____

4 Jessica has been very tired. She has slept only 6 hours every night for the past 7 nights. How many hours has she slept total?
Set up: _____
Solution: _____

5 The Sacramento Kings scored 112 points in their game on Monday. Then they scored an unknown number of points in their game on Thursday. If they scored a total of 205 points in the two games, how many points did they score in the game on Thursday?
Set up: _____
Solution: _____

Using Information

87

⭐ **Tables** are used to display information in a quick, organized way.

How many pets does Megan have? Find Megan and look to the right under cats and dogs.
2 cats +1 dog = 3 pets

Pets Owned by Club Critter Members

Friend	Cats	Dogs
Megan	2	1
Jake	5	2
Kyle	0	4
Carlos	3	3
Brianne	1	2

Use the table above to answer questions 1–3.

1 Who doesn't have any cats?
_____

Who has the most pets?
_____

2 Who has an equal number of cats and dogs?
_____

How many cats do Brianne and Kyle have combined?
_____

3 Who has 1 more dog than cat?
_____

How many pets do the friends have altogether?
_____

Use the table about populations of different towns in 1990 and 2000 to answer questions 4–5.

Populations

Town	Population in 1990	Population in 2000
Brownsburg	540	430
Huntington	690	720
Yorktown	250	250
Drake	360	960
Cunningham	200	400

4 Which town had the lowest population in 1990?
_____

For which town did the population not change during the ten years?
_____

5 Which towns did not increase in size from 1990 to 2000?
_____

Which town saw the largest population increase?
_____

Using Information

88

⭐ **Bar graphs** also display information in an organized way.

How many students in Mrs. Smith's class like apples most? Since the bar for apples is between 6 and 8, the answer is 7.

Favorite Fruits of Mrs. Smith's Students

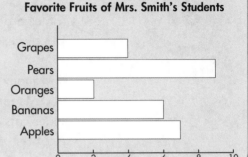

Answer questions 1–4 using the bar graph above.

1 Which is the most popular fruit among the students in Mrs. Smith's class?
_____

2 How many students like oranges most? _____

3 How many **more** students like bananas than grapes? _____

4 What is the total number of students who prefer apples **and** pears? _____

This is a **line graph.** Use the line graph to answer questions 5–7.

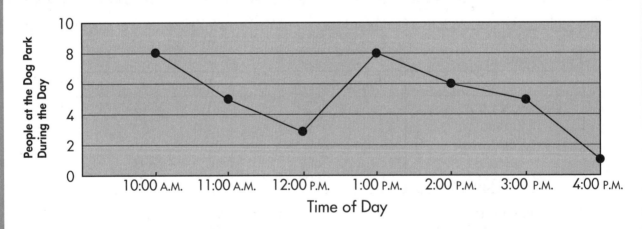

5 How many people take their dogs to the park at 11:00 A.M.? _____

6 What time of the day is the least popular time to visit the dog park? _____

7 How many people visit the dog park between 10:00 A.M. and 4:00 P.M.? _____

Name _____

Comparing Information

89

Answer the questions using the graphs.

Graph A
Video Sales on Tuesday

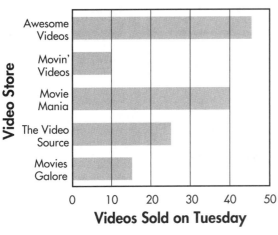

Graph B
Videos Sold This Week at Awesome Videos

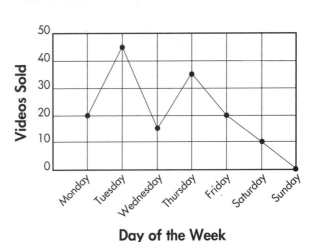

1. Which graph would you use to find out how many videos were sold at Movies Galore on Tuesday? _____

2. How many videos were sold at Movin' Videos on Tuesday? _____

3. Which is the most popular day of the week to buy videos at Awesome Videos? _____

4. Which video store sells the lowest number of videos on Tuesday? _____

5. How many more videos are sold at Movie Mania on Tuesday than at Awesome Videos on Thursday? _____

6. Which chart can you use to determine how many videos were sold at Awesome Videos on Tuesday? _____

7. Create a bar graph with your classmates. Ask 10 other students how many people there are in their families. Then fill in the bar graph.

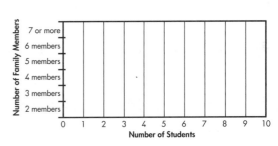

Name _____

Circle Graphs

90

⭐ This is a **circle graph.** It represents a survey that some kids did at their school. They asked all the kids at the school what they eat for breakfast.

What fraction of the kids eat yogurt for breakfast? $\frac{2}{10}$ or $\frac{1}{5}$

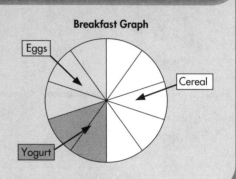

Breakfast Graph

Eggs

Cereal

Yogurt

Use what you know about fractions to answer the questions about the graph.

1 What fraction of the kids eat eggs for breakfast? _____

2 What fraction of the kids do NOT eat cereal for breakfast? _____

3 What fraction of the kids eat either cereal or eggs for breakfast? _____

This circle graph represents where people in the Fishing Club are from. Answer questions 4–6 using the graph.

Number of People in the Fishing Club from Each State

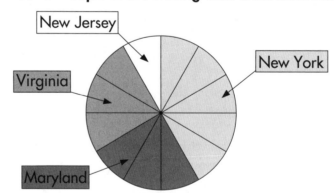

New Jersey

New York

Virginia

Maryland

4 What fraction of the Fishing Club members come from New York? _____

5 What fraction of the club members are NOT from New Jersey? _____

6 What fraction of the club members are from Virginia **and** Maryland combined? _____

Advantage Math Grade 4 © 2004 Creative Teaching Press

Mean, Median, and Mode

91

	What is it?	How do I find it?	What is it for Set A?
Mean	The average	Add the numbers and divide by the amount of numbers	$(2 + 2 + 7 + 9 + 10 + 12) \div 6 = \mathbf{7}$
Median	The middle	If amount of digits is an odd number: the middle number. If amount of digits is an even number: find the average of the 2 middle numbers	$(7 + 9) \div 2 = \mathbf{8}$
Mode	The most common	Find the numbers that occur most often (can be more than one number)	**2**

Set A: 2, 2, 7, 9, 10, 12

Find the mean, median, and mode for each set.

1 9, 11, 11, 13, 16
Mean: _____
Median: _____
Mode: _____

      7, 9, 10, 14, 16, 16
Mean: _____
Median: _____
Mode: _____

2 1, 1, 6, 12, 12, 13
Mean: _____
Median: _____
Mode: _____

      20, 22, 22, 31, 35
Mean: _____
Median: _____
Mode: _____

---

3 Armando scored 86, 74, and 92 on his three math tests last month. What was his mean score? _____

4 The babies weigh 18 lbs, 27 lbs, 21 lbs, and 23 lbs. What is the median weight of the four babies? _____

Name _____

⭐ The **range** of a set of terms is the highest term minus the lowest term.

Set B: 6, 10, 21, 40
Range: 40 − 6 = 34

What is the range on the *y*-axis of
the set of points on the graph?
Range: 12 − 4 = 8

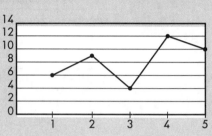

Find the ranges.

1   67, 54, 23, 48
Range: _____

102, 51, 2, 17, 34
Range: _____

2   6, 19, 3
Range: _____

102, 103, 104, 105
Range: _____

3

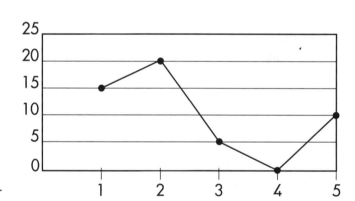

Range of the *y* values: _____

4

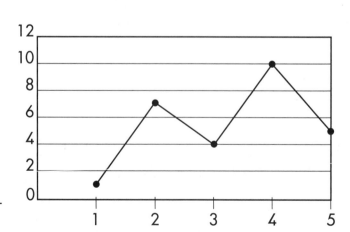

Range of the *y* values: _____

Combinations

93

⭐ Martha brought 3 shirts (blue, yellow, and pink) and 2 pairs of pants (jeans and khakis) on the trip. How many outfits can she create?
Find the combinations: multiply the number of shirts by the number of pants.
$3 \times 2 = 6$ outfits

	Jeans	Khakis
Blue shirt	Blue shirt and jeans	Blue shirt and khakis
Yellow shirt	Yellow shirt and jeans	Yellow shirt and khakis
Pink shirt	Pink shirt and jeans	Pink shirt and khakis

Solve the combination problems. Fill in the tables with the possible combinations. Hint: use abbreviations if necessary.

1. Linda has 4 pairs of shoes (sandals, tennis shoes, hiking boots, and dress shoes) and 4 different boxes to store them in (small, medium, medium-large, and large). How many different combinations of shoe pairs and boxes can she make?

    _____

2. Joe can't decide how to decorate his living room. He has 2 couches (large and small) and 5 covers (black, white, brown, striped, and plaid) to decorate them with. How many possible couch decorating combinations are there? _____

3. Aunt Susan has 5 necklaces and 5 pairs of earrings to wear with them. How many different ways can she wear her jewelry? _____

Name _____

Possible Outcomes

94

⭐ Before we look at probabilities, figure out the possible outcomes for a situation.

This chart shows who is responsible for taking the garbage out on the different days of the week. List the people who could possibly take out the garbage.
Answer: Wesley, Mary, Phil (we don't need to list each one again)

Day of the Week	Family Member
Sunday	Wesley
Monday	Mary
Tuesday	Phil
Wednesday	Phil
Thursday	Mary
Friday	Phil
Saturday	Wesley

Solve.

1 This is a list of the kids in Coach George's swimming class:

Jim 10   Tim 9
Bobby 9   Kevin 12
Lisa 11   Nikki 9
Luis 10   Christina 8

List the different ages of the swimmers. _____

2 These are the items in Terry's bag:

If Terry reaches into her bag and pulls out 3 things, list the possible combinations of things she could grab. _____

_____

_____

3 If Troy spins the spinner twice, what are all of the possible combinations of letters on which the spinner could land? (One combination is M, M.)

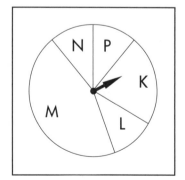

_____

_____

_____

Probability

95

 Probability tells how likely an event is to happen.

Use the following rule to determine the probability of an event:

Probability = $\dfrac{\text{number of ways the event could happen}}{\text{the total number of possibilities}}$

What is the probability that the spinner will land on a vowel?
Think: A and E are the only vowels and there are 5 equal-sized places the spinner could land.
Probability of Vowel: $\dfrac{2}{5}$

Find the probabilities. Reduce fractions to their lowest terms.

1 The die has six faces numbered 1–6. In order for Janine to get to move her player forward, she has to roll an odd number. What are the chances that she will move? _____

2 Hank flipped a coin. On the first 5 flips, he has gotten tails, tails, heads, tails, heads. What is the probability that he will get tails on the 6th flip?
_____

3 What is the probability that the spinner will land on 7?
_____

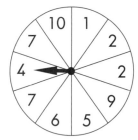

4 Dice are numbered 1–6. Danny is going to roll one 3 times. If he totals the numbers that he gets each time, what is the highest total that he could get?
_____

5 In order to win the game, Jamal has to land on a 6 or higher. What is the probability that he will win?
_____

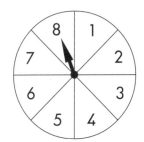

Name _____

Predicting Outcomes

96

Predict the outcome. Remember to reduce fractions to their lowest terms.

1. Jack reached into a bag of marbles. If there were 8 red marbles and 12 blue marbles, what is the probability that he got a red marble? _____

2. Chantelle wrote each letter of the word **Connecticut** on different cards, then turned them face down on the table. If Tanner chooses a card, what is the probability that he will choose the letter **c**? _____

3. In his bag of plastic animals, Kenny has 15 elephants, 10 penguins, 13 zebras, and 17 monkeys. If Kenny chooses an animal without looking, what is the probability that he will choose an elephant? _____

4. In a deck of cards, there is an equal number of hearts, diamonds, clubs, and spades. If you pull a card out of a deck, what is the probability that it will be a diamond? _____

5. In the movie theater, there are 9 rows of seats with 10 seats in each row. The seats are numbered starting with 1. If you buy a ticket to the next movie, what is the probability that you will sit in a seat that is a multiple of 10? _____

6. Faith had 4 dresses, 8 shirts, 2 skirts, and 2 pairs of pants hanging in her closet. What is the probability that she could reach in without looking and pull out a shirt? _____

Name _____

Practice Test

97

Test-Taking Tip: Try to stay relaxed during the test. Roll your shoulders to relax yourself.

Fill in the bubble beside the correct answer.

---

1 Which of the following numbers is five million, two hundred eighty-four thousand, twenty-six and nine hundredths?

- ○ 528,427.9
- ○ 5,248,026.9
- ○ 5,284,026.09
- ○ 5,284,260.09

2 Which of the following is nine hundredths?

- ○ $\frac{9}{900}$
- ○ $\frac{9}{10}$
- ○ $\frac{9}{100}$
- ○ $\frac{4}{10}$

3 $\frac{4}{10}$ =

- ○ 0.8
- ○ 0.4
- ○ 0.08
- ○ 0.04

4 Which number is XI?

- ○ 11
- ○ 19
- ○ 16
- ○ 21

5 How much money is shown?

- ○ $7.26
- ○ $8.16
- ○ $8.26
- ○ $7.16

6 10 x 12 =

- ○ 0
- ○ 100
- ○ 120
- ○ 1012

7 $\frac{4}{5} + \frac{3}{5}$ =

- ○ $1\frac{2}{5}$
- ○ $\frac{7}{10}$
- ○ $1\frac{3}{5}$
- ○ $1\frac{1}{5}$

8 7.26 + 11.59 =

- ○ 18.75
- ○ 17.76
- ○ 17.86
- ○ 18.85

Name _____

98

Fill in the bubble beside the correct answer.

---

1 Which property of multiplication is shown here?
(15 x 23) x 29 = 15 x (23 x 29)
- ○ commutative
- ○ distributive
- ○ associative
- ○ identity

5 Which answer is 63,571 rounded to the nearest thousand?
- ○ 64,000
- ○ 60,000
- ○ 63,600
- ○ 63,570

---

2 Greg bought 8 packages of crackers. If each package has 21 crackers, how many crackers does he have in all?
- ○ 29
- ○ 168
- ○ 2 R5
- ○ 169

6 Ray is counting by thousands and he has reached 60,000. What is the next multiple of 1,000?
- ○ 70,000
- ○ 600,000
- ○ 61,000
- ○ 6,000

---

3 Antonia has 384 coins in her coin collection. She keeps the coins in 6 jars. If there is an equal number of coins in each jar, how many are there in a jar?
- ○ 64 coins
- ○ 390 coins
- ○ 63 coins
- ○ 128 coins

7 All of these numbers are multiples of 9 EXCEPT _____.
- ○ 351
- ○ 783
- ○ 366
- ○ 765

---

4 There was $\frac{7}{12}$ of a pizza left over. Peg ate $\frac{1}{4}$ of the pizza for dinner. How much of the pizza is left?
- ○ $\frac{5}{6}$
- ○ $\frac{5}{12}$
- ○ $\frac{1}{4}$
- ○ $\frac{1}{3}$

8 Which number is NOT a perfect square?
- ○ 81
- ○ 49
- ○ 54
- ○ 36

Practice Test

99

Fill in the bubble beside the correct answer.

---

1 How long is the pencil?

○ $3\frac{3}{4}$ in. ○ $3\frac{5}{8}$ in.

○ $3\frac{5}{8}$ cm ○ $3\frac{1}{2}$ in.

---

2 What is the volume of this box?

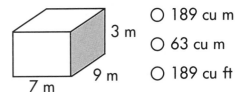

3 m
9 m
7 m

○ 19 sq m

○ 189 cu m

○ 63 cu m

○ 189 cu ft

---

3 420 minutes =

○ 7 hours

○ 2 days

○ 2500 seconds

○ 1 day

---

4 Which of the following is a metric measurement?

○ 51°F

○ 83 g

○ 14 oz

○ 90°

---

5 Which pair of numbers is the perimeter and the area of the rectangle?

8 cm
21 cm

○ 29 cm, 168 cu cm

○ 58 cu cm, 168 cm

○ 29 cm, 58 cu cm

○ 58 cm, 168 sq cm

---

6 The school dance is on the third Friday of May. If the first Friday of May is May 2, what is the date of the dance?

○ May 12

○ May 16

○ May 21

○ May 23

---

7 How many edges does this figure have?

○ 3

○ 5

○ 6

○ 9

---

8 What is this shape called?

○ heptilateral

○ octagon

○ hexagon

○ heptagon

Practice Test

100

Fill in the bubble beside the correct answer.

1 If point C were moved 2 to the left and 1 unit down, what would be its coordinates?

- ○ (5, 3)
- ○ (1, 3)
- ○ (3, 4)
- ○ (1, 5)

5 8, 8, 11, 16, 22
Which pair of numbers represents the mean and median of the set of numbers?

- ○ 13, 11
- ○ 8, 14
- ○ 8, 11
- ○ 11, 13

2 Which figure is congruent to M?

- ○
- ○
- ○
- ○

6 Jake is taking 5 pairs of socks and 3 pairs of shoes to his cousin's house. How many combinations of the socks and shoes can he create?

- ○ 15
- ○ 8
- ○ 10
- ○ 25

3 Hannah has 5 boxes of equal numbers of books. She has 75 books total, but she can't remember how many books are in each box. Which expression shows an equation for this situation?

- ○ $5+n=75$
- ○ $5n=75$
- ○ $5÷n=75$
- ○ $n-5=75$

7 What kind of angle is shown?

- ○ straight
- ○ acute
- ○ obtuse
- ○ right

4 A and B are:

Input	Output
A	54
2	12
5	30
12	72
1	**B**
7	42

- ○ 8 and 10
- ○ 9 and 6
- ○ 7 and 0
- ○ 9 and 1

8 What is the probability of spinning a multiple of 5?

- ○ $\frac{3}{10}$
- ○ $\frac{2}{5}$
- ○ $\frac{1}{2}$
- ○ $\frac{4}{5}$

Name _____

Math Grade 4 Tracking Sheet

Activity	Possible	My Score
Unit 1		
1	12	
2	7	
3	6	
4	8	
5	12	
6	12	
7	16	
8	14	
9	4	
10	12	
11	10	
12	6	
13	12	
14	13	
Test Scores		
15	8	
16	8	
Unit 2		
17	13	
18	14	
19	12	
20	12	
21	17	
22	11	
23	10	
24	12	
25	10	
26	12	
27	12	

Activity	Possible	My Score
28	11	
Test Scores		
29	8	
30	8	
Unit 3		
31	36	
32	26	
33	26	
34	21	
35	21	
36	14	
37	8	
38	8	
39	29	
40	29	
41	20	
42	25	
43	27	
44	14	
45	13	
46	20	
47	19	
48	18	
49	18	
50	19	
51	7	
52	5	
53	26	
54	8	
Test Scores		

Activity	Possible	My Score
55	8	
56	8	
Unit 4		
57	5	
58	8	
59	8	
60	7	
61	17	
62	17	
63	12	
64	6	
65	8	
66	8	
67	11	
68	8	
Test Scores		
69	8	
70	8	
Unit 5		
71	13	
72	7	
73	9	
74	8	
75	6	
76	6	
77	6	
78	10	
79	10	
80	6	
Test Scores		

Activity	Possible	My Score
81	8	
82	8	
Unit 6		
83	9	
84	12	
85	12	
86	5	
87	10	
88	7	
89	7	
90	6	
91	14	
92	6	
93	3	
94	3	
95	5	
96	6	
Test Scores		
97	8	
98	8	
99	8	
100	8	

Math 4 Answer Key

Activity 1
1. 7 hundred thousand
2. thousands
3. 8
4. 9
5. 5,479
6. 702,899
7. 6,450,021
8. two thousand, three hundred fifty-six
9. one million, two hundred nine thousand, four hundred eleven
10. four hundred thousand, eight hundred ninety-seven
11. 3,452
12. 12,209

Activity 2
1. $^{13}/_{25}$ $4^{1}/_{2}$
2. $^{27}/_{100}$ $3^{5}/_{6}$
3. three-tenths

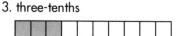

4. four and three-fourths

5. 3/5 or three-fifths

Activity 3
1. 0.41, $^{41}/_{100}$ 4.9, $4^{9}/_{10}$
2. $2^{8}/_{10}$
3. $1^{3}/_{100}$
4. $^{1}/_{10}$
5. $^{7}/_{10}$

Activity 4
1. $^{2}/_{5}$, $^{4}/_{10}$
   $^{3}/_{4}$, $^{6}/_{8}$
2. $^{4}/_{6}$, $^{2}/_{3}$
   $^{3}/_{9}$, $^{2}/_{6}$
3. $^{4}/_{8}$, $^{5}/_{10}$, $^{6}/_{12}$ $^{8}/_{12}$, $^{6}/_{9}$, $^{4}/_{6}$
4. $^{9}/_{15}$, $^{12}/_{20}$, $^{15}/_{25}$, $^{18}/_{30}$ $^{6}/_{18}$, $^{5}/_{15}$, $^{4}/_{12}$

Activity 5
1. $^{1}/_{2}$ $^{3}/_{5}$ $^{3}/_{5}$ $^{3}/_{5}$
2. $^{1}/_{3}$ $^{1}/_{10}$ $^{7}/_{12}$ $^{1}/_{3}$
3. cross out $^{5}/_{10}$ circle $^{2}/_{3}$
4. cross out $^{3}/_{15}$ circle $^{1}/_{4}$
5. cross out $^{2}/_{10}$ circle $^{1}/_{2}$
6. cross out $^{1}/_{10}$ circle $^{2}/_{5}$

Activity 6
1. $0.5 = {}^{5}/_{10} = {}^{1}/_{2}$
   $0.2 = {}^{2}/_{10} = {}^{1}/_{5}$
2. $0.75 = {}^{75}/_{100} = {}^{3}/_{4}$
   $0.15 = {}^{15}/_{100} = {}^{3}/_{20}$
3. $^{6}/_{10} = {}^{3}/_{5}$ $^{5}/_{10} = {}^{1}/_{2}$
4. $^{10}/_{100} = {}^{1}/_{10}$ $^{55}/_{100} = {}^{11}/_{20}$
5. $^{5}/_{100} = {}^{1}/_{20}$ $^{25}/_{100} = {}^{1}/_{4}$
6. $1^{4}/_{10} = 1^{2}/_{5}$ $3^{8}/_{10} = 3^{4}/_{5}$

Activity 7
1. <   >
2. =   <
3. <   <
4. >   >
5. >   <
6. 3, 51, 25 + 27, 112
7. 1, 2 + 3, 8, 11
8. 27, 72, 50 + 43, 94
9. 14, 28, 28 + 10, 55
10. 49; 149; 3,049; 3,490
11. 17, 71, 107, 170, 701

Activity 8
1. >   =
2. <   <
3. <   <
4. >   >
5. <   >
6. =   =
7. $^{7}/_{10} = 0.7$ $^{5}/_{10} = 0.5$

Activity 9
missing numbers listed only
5.2, 5.5, 5.8, 6.0
20, 50, 60
20, 35, 50, 60
$2^{3}/_{4}$, 3, $3^{1}/_{4}$, 4

Activity 10
1. five hundred ten thousand, two hundred and three-tenths
eight and seventeen twenty-fifths

2. 648,900.67 $21^{3}/_{4}$
3.

4. <   =
5. >   <
6. $^{3}/_{5}$, $^{4}/_{5}$, $^{5}/_{5}$, $1^{1}/_{5}$, $1^{2}/_{5}$, $1^{3}/_{5}$, $1^{4}/_{5}$, $^{10}/_{5}$, $2^{1}/_{5}$, $2^{2}/_{5}$, $2^{3}/_{5}$, $2^{4}/_{5}$, $^{15}/_{5}$
0.6, 0.8, 1.0, 1.2, 1.4, 1.6, 1.8, 2.0, 2.2, 2.4, 2.6, 2.8, 3.0

Activity 11
1. $1.79
2. $8.25
3. $24.33
4. $10.65
5.

0	4	1	1	0	1
0	3	0	1	0	4
1	3	0	0	1	2
0	2	2	1	0	0
1	0	2	0	1	2
1	4	1	0	1	2

Activity 12
1. $3.41 + $3.34 = $6.75
2. $1.70 + $4.28 = $5.98
3. $2.07 + $4.85 = $6.92
4. $5.93
5. $5.78 − $3.25 = $2.53
6. $4.80 − $0.60 = $4.20

Activity 13
1. 20,000 + 1,000 + 600 + 50 + 7
2. 500,000 + 40,000 + 30 + 1
3. 7,000,000 + 100,000 + 20,000 + 3,000 + 900 + 70
4. 6,000 + 700
5. 9,000,438
6. 2,108
7. 310,000
8. 79,054
9. two hundred
10. 7
11. six hundredths
12. 0

Activity 14
1. VI   XXX   MMM
2. XXIX   XVIII   DII
3. 150   400   35
4. 600   14   40
5. 1,000 + 500 + 100 + 100 + 50 + 10 + 10 + 5 + 1 = 1776

Activity 15—Take a Test Drive
1. 6,702,031
2. 840,065.23
3. ³⁄₅
4. ⁷⁄₅
5. >
6. =
7. >
8. ²⁄₅

Activity 16—Take a Test Drive
1. $0.87
2. $40.48
3. 0.27
4. 90
5. 5,000,000 + 600,000 + 1,000 + 80 + 4
6. 400,267
7. $1.18
8. XVI

Activity 17
1. 40   2,000
2. 530   7,000
3. 8,700   70
4. 800   97,000
5. 400   1,000
6. 300 animals
7. 5,300 feet
8. 90 cards

Activity 18
1. 35,000   800,000
2. 700,000 51,300
3. 6,100   976,510
4. 570,000 200,000
5. 40,000   73,300
6. 708,000 70,000
7. 500,000 people
8. 40,000 people

Activity 19
1. yes   no
2. no   yes
3. no   yes
4. no   yes

5. 1, 2, 3, 5, 6, 10, 15, 30
6. 9, 18, 27, 36, 45, 54, 63, 72, 81, 90, 99
7. 36
8. No, because 78 is not a multiple of 8.

Activity 20
1. 1, 2, 3, 4, 6, 12
2. 1, 2, 3, 6
3. 1
4. 1
5. 3
6. 8, 16, 24, 32, 40, 48, 56, 64, 72, 80
7. 24, 48
8. 12
9. 60
10. 24
11. No, because 42 is not a multiple of 8.
12. Yes, she will have 5 cards in each group (5 is a factor of 25).

Activity 21
1. 60   140
2. 280   800
3. 2,390 5,460
4. 450   100   220
5. 1,030 300   270
6. 70   710   990
7. 130
8. 70

Activity 22
1. 600   8,000
2. 1,800 65,000
3. 5,050 9,000
4. cross out 21, write 30
5. cross out 616, write 615
6. cross out 1,100, write 1,000
7. 1,700
8. 6,000

Activity 23
1. no   yes
2. yes   no
3. both   both
4. 2   both
5. no
6. no

Activity 24
1. yes   no
2. yes   yes
3. 330   117
4. 105   6,021
5. 51   29
6. no
7. He could pack 3 boxes with 15 books each or 15 boxes with 5 books each. Or, he could pack 5 boxes with 9 books in each or 9 boxes with 5 books in each.

Activity 25
1. 7 x 7 = 49   5 x 5 = 25
2. 10 x 10 = 100   1 x 1 = 1
3.

    16   64   9

4.

    36   4   121

Activity 26
1. 4 9 16 25
2. 36 49 64 81
3. 9 patches
4. 49 tiles
5. 3
6. 36 blocks

Activity 27
1. 380
2. 58,000
3. 57,500
4. 500
5. 1, 2, 4, 5, 10, 20
6. yes
7. 4
8. 30
9. no
10. 130, 150
11. yes
12. 3,030; 4,030; 6,030

Activity 28
1. 10,000
2. 10
3. 3
4. 1, 2, 3, 4, 6, 8, or 9
5. 81

6. 8
7. 9
8. 56
9. 39
10.

11.

Activity 29—Take a Test Drive
1. 405,000
2. 700,000
3. 705
4. 9
5. 60
6. No, 9 tubes with 9 balls and one with 5
7. 1,470
8. 75,000; 85,000; 95,000

Activity 30—Take a Test Drive
1. 5
2. 10
3. 49
4. 4
5. 3
6. 49
7. 1, 2, 5, 10
8. 25

Activity 31
1. 11   17   11   13
2. 28   29   3   8
3. 7   9   8   11
4. 59   88   98   69   77   79
5. 45   34   4   30   25   10
6. 748 985 279 989 988 898
7. 421 201 523 127 233 42

Activity 32
1. 91   74   90   51   89   85
2. 58   13   45   45   9   17
3. 755 960 780 777 282 519
4. 165 191 246 291 254 402
5. 67 students
6. 181 students

Activity 33
1. 770   627   798
   882   1,027 696
2. 254   105   572
   367   171   105
3. 5,870 9,516 22,018

   59,165 87,402 70,517
4. 6,872 3,099 40,210
   15,181 57,902 29,891
5. 69 parents
6. 462 people

Activity 34
1. 11.90 31.75 9.91
   25.17 29.56 36.49
2. 39.61 17.43 61.00
   57.56 60.31 79.76
3. 22.53 22.84 69.45
   68.80 0.70   2.23
4. $5.92
5. 8.20 miles
6. 1.50 pounds

Activity 35
1. 6.62   71.09 77.27
   21.08 21.26 10.94
2. 5.51   9.21   20.53
   13.31 11.41 18.12
3. 2.80   54.19 0.16
   67.28 11.98 12.67
4. $6.45
5. 0.08 meter
6. 3.51 pounds

Activity 36
1. $11/7 = 1\frac{4}{7}$
   $14/10 = 1\frac{4}{10} = 1\frac{2}{5}$
2. $12/9 = 1\frac{3}{9} = 1\frac{1}{3}$
   $20/16 = 1\frac{4}{16} = 1\frac{1}{4}$
3. $9/6 = 1\frac{3}{6} = 1\frac{1}{2}$ $12/11 = 1\frac{1}{11}$
4. $7/21 = \frac{1}{3}$ $2/18 = \frac{1}{9}$
5. $6/13$ $6/9 = \frac{2}{3}$
6. $10/20 = \frac{1}{2}$ $10/15 = \frac{2}{3}$
7. $7/49 = \frac{1}{7}$ $\frac{1}{10}$

Activity 37
1. $\frac{(2\times4)}{(3\times4)} + \frac{(3\times3)}{(4\times3)} = \frac{8}{12} + \frac{9}{12} = \frac{17}{12} = 1\frac{5}{12}$
2. $\frac{7}{8} - \frac{(1\times2)}{(4\times2)} = \frac{7}{8} - \frac{2}{8} = \frac{5}{8}$
3. $\frac{2}{6} + \frac{1}{6} = \frac{3}{6} = \frac{1}{2}$
   $\frac{11}{12} - \frac{3}{12} = \frac{8}{12} = \frac{2}{3}$
4. $\frac{5}{5} = 1$ $\frac{8}{10} - \frac{3}{10} = \frac{5}{10} = \frac{1}{2}$
5. $\frac{1}{2} + \frac{4}{5} = \frac{5}{10} + \frac{8}{10} = \frac{13}{10} = 1\frac{3}{10}$ cups
6. $\frac{8}{9} - \frac{1}{3} = \frac{8}{9} - \frac{3}{9} = \frac{5}{9}$ less

Activity 38
1. 0   zero property of multiplication

2. 8   commutative property of addition
3. 8   associative property of addition
4. 1   identity property of multiplication
5. 8   6   distributive property of multiplication
6. 4   associative property of multiplication
7. 0   identity property of addition
8. 6   commutative property of multiplication

Activity 39
1. 4   3   49   4
2. 56   27   12   25
3. 64   12   30   35   9   24
4. 24   0   21   63   25   40
5. 48   36   42   24   0   45
6. 72 cards
7. 90 blueberries
8. 42 acorns

Activity 40
1. 4   3   8   5
2. 4   6   25   7
3. 8   9   6   10   1   9
4. 3   8   7   8   4   9
5. 8   5   7   4   10   8
6. $5
7. 10 days
8. 9 pages

Activity 41
1. $6/16 = \frac{3}{8}$ $5/14$
2. 859 344 321 198 785 180
3. 81.35 18.17 12.23
   25.3   14,828 75,864
4. $\frac{2}{3}$ $4/8 = \frac{1}{2}$
5. $\frac{3}{4} - \frac{2}{4} = \frac{1}{4}$ $\frac{12}{15} - \frac{10}{15} = \frac{2}{15}$
6. $\frac{3}{12} + \frac{2}{12} = \frac{5}{12}$ $\frac{6}{8} + \frac{1}{8} = \frac{7}{8}$

Activity 42
1. 48   9   8   4
2. 21   12   7   4
3. 80   6   36   2   27   4
4. 9   28   10   0   1   60
5. 3   C
   9   I
   7   I
   6   C
   0   Z

Activity 43
1. 135   180   105
   320   146   84
2. 57   288   94
   1,368   2,088   700
3. 856   1,737   4,600
   2,289   618   4,278
4. 716   803   789
   19,585   34,692   7,145
5. 1,550 burritos
6. $2,088
7. 1,050 peanuts

Activity 44
1. 1,196   2,556   756
   3,240   2,075   4,736
2. 48,116   65,992   23,002
   454,720   23,985   60,478
3. $5,076
4. $4,935

Activity 45
1. 69,660   49,980   168,976
   140,990   90,870   215,586
2. 68,250   299,156   101,558
   449,540   478,880   407,778
3. $38,400

Activity 46
1. 219   513   21,736
   1,012   9,772   29,854
2. 6,842   8,541   5,238
   3,840   11,720   4,616
3. 11,134   279,027   40,271
   97,578   169,344   715,355
4. 1,620 miles
5. 61,020 miles

Activity 47
1. 24   15   13   11   87   17
2. 28   12   13   13   15   10
3. 11   14   36   25   261   114
4. $13 each

Activity 48
1. 13   14   16   79   16   30
2. 28   34   43   89   24   23
3. 46   111   231   78   30   24

Activity 49
1. 302   308   123
   320   231   342
2. 137   601   2937
   754   243   342

3. 751   458   347
   681   370   124

Activity 50
1. 12   11   15   16   15   12
2. 164   105   75   42   45   83
3. 741   98   137   741   470   856
4. 22 books

Activity 51
1. 8 racks
2. 280 cards
3. 4 trays
4. 24 muffins
5. 3 muffins
6. $84
7. 13 kids

Activity 52
1. Step 1: Add the number of baggies: 10 + 20 = 30
Step 2: Divide baggies by family members:
30 ÷ 5 = 6 baggies each
2. Step 1: Find how many beads she has: 5 x 8 = 40 beads
Step 2: Divide the beads by the number of necklaces:
40 ÷ 4 = 10 beads on each
3. Step 1: Add the miles they drove away from home:
108.3 + 56.7 = 165 miles
Step 2: Subtract the miles they drove back:
165 − 8.6 = 156.4 miles
4. Step 1: Subtract how much Cody ate of the first bag:
$^{11}/_{12} - ^{7}/_{12} = ^{4}/_{12}$ $(^{1}/_3)$
Step 2: Add the amount left in the first bag to the second bag:
$^{4}/_{12} + ^{5}/_{12} = ^{9}/_{12} = ^{3}/_4$ bag of pretzels
5. Step 1: Add the marbles:
76 + 12 = 88
Step 2: Divide the amount by the number of boxes:
88 ÷ 4 = 22 marbles in each

Activity 53
1. 141   12   30.27
   1,769   29   15
2. 2,520   850   21
   46   2,469   2.59
3. 74   1,265   1,898
   38,052   1,224   683

4. 782   155,914   347
   9,184   4,072   455,480
5. 168 tickets
6. $24 each

Activity 54
1. $105
2. 168, with one person driving 3 more miles (171 miles)
3. 512 bars
4. 13 times
5. 690 pages
6. 13 miles
7. $1.53
8. $^{3}/_6 + ^{5}/_6 = ^{8}/_6 = 1^{2}/_6 = 1^{1}/_3$ jars

Activity 55 — Take a Test Drive
1. 88
2. $^{2}/_9$
3. $1^{1}/_2$
4. 3.29
5. 21.8 pounds
6. 16.05
7. 9 (8 + 3) = (9 x 8) + (9 x 3)
8. $^{5}/_8$

Activity 56 — Take a Test Drive
1. 85
2. 26
3. 67,425
4. $62
5. 23
6. 777
7. 5442
8. 9156

Activity 57
1. 2⅜ in.
2. 3¼ in.
3. 4½ in.
4. 1⅛ in.
5. 5 feet

Activity 58
1. 34 in.
2. 28 yd
3. 32 ft
4. 28 ft
5. 24 ft
6. 22 in.
7. 30 ft
8. 100 in.

Activity 59
1. 45 sq in. 96 sq in.
2. 18 sq in. 35 sq in.
3. 28 sq ft 36 sq in.
4. 60 sq ft
5. 144 sq ft

Activity 60
1. 120 cu in.   240 cu ft
2. 189 cu in.   256 cu ft
3. 30 cu ft
4. 3 ft
5. 250 cu cm

Activity 61
1. 3   3
2. 5   48
3. 4, 10   2, 12
4. minutes   seconds
5. minutes   hours
6. days   seconds
   story: minute seconds
   hours   days   hours

Activity 62
1. 4   12
2. 4   days
3. years   years
4. weeks   centuries
5. years   weeks
6. weeks   years
   story: months years
   centuries days   weeks

Activity 63
1. obtuse   acute   straight
2. acute   right   obtuse
3. acute   acute   obtuse
4. right
5. acute
6. 180°

Activity 64
1. ∠ LMN   120°
2. 30°   135°
3.
   45°
   45°   90°
4. 90° 90°
   90° 90°

Activity 65
1. 27°C   3 lbs
2. 60 sq m   2¾ in.
3. 85°F   8 oz.
4. 4 kg   12.5 mi

Activity 66
1. Celsius
2. lbs., in., feet
3. meters, metric
4. standard, feet
5. straight, right
6. length: m, cm weight: kg, g
7. 24 m, 35 sq m
8. 6 ft

Activity 67
1. 192 cu m
   perimeter: 28 ft
   area: 40 sq ft
2. perimeter: 58 cm
   area: 180 sq cm
   volume: 108 cu ft
3. seconds, hours, days, weeks,
   years, centuries
4.
   right   90°
5.
   acute   45°
6.
   straight   180°
7.
   obtuse   105°

Activity 68
1. Saturday
2. 2nd
3. 21st
4. 21 days
5. 3 hrs
6. 7:15 A.M. 4:45 P.M.
7. Saturday or Sunday
8. no

Activity 69 — Take a Test Drive
1. 1½ in.
2. 60 cm
3. 30 sq ft
4. 360 cu cm
5. minutes
6. 3

7. 4
8. 135°

Activity 70 — Take a Test Drive
1. 40°
2. lbs
3. >
4. 36 oz
5. °F
6. 28 sq ft
7. 2 ft by 3 ft by 2 ft
8. 5

Activity 71
1. 3, 6, 12, 8
2. 2, 15
3. faces or sides, vertices or
   points, dimensions
4. Answers will vary. One possible
   drawing is a line.
5. Answers will vary. One possible
   drawing is a triangle.
6. Answers will vary. One possible
   drawing is a sphere.

Activity 72
1.

2. pentagon octagon rectangle
3. Answers will vary. Some
   possible answers include:
   octopus, October, polygon,
   pentagram, triple, trio, trinity,
   tricycle, quadruple, quadruplets.

Activity 73
1. similar   similar   not similar
2. not similar similar   not similar
3. Answers will vary. One possible
   drawing is a rectangle and a
   square.
4. Drawing should be of a large
   pentagon and a smaller
   pentagon.
5. Answers will vary. One possible
   drawing is a pyramid.

Activity 74
1. not congruent
   not congruent
   congruent
2. not congruent
   congruent

not congruent

3.

4.

Activity 75
1.
2.
3.

Activity 76
1. 180°   180°
2. 0°   180°
3. 180°

Activity 77
1. (2, 3) (4, 4)
2. (6, 8) 4
3. 5 (6, 5)

Activity 78

Activity 79
1. 45 sq m
2. 84 in.
3. 270 sq m
4. 330 m
5 Perimeter: 16 in.

Area: 16 sq in.
6. bottom left: (1, 1)
   bottom right: (3, 1)
   top left: (1, 5)
   top right: (3, 5)

Activity 80
1. 224 sq ft
2. 900 yd
3. $270
4. 27 liters
5. 192 in.

6. $648 − $600 = $48 more

Activity 81 — Take a Test Drive
1. 8
2. 10 cm
3. octagon
4. 5
5.
6.
7. 30
8.

Activity 82 — Take a Test Drive
1. flipped images
2. 90° clockwise
3. 0°
4. (0, 4)
5. A
6. (3, 3)
7. 45 ft

Activity 83
1. Pattern: ⁺3, ⁺2, ⁺3, ⁺2, . . .
   Next number: 17
   Pattern: ⁺1, ⁺2, ⁺3, ⁺4, . . .
   Next number: 22
2. Pattern: x2
   Next number: 64
   Pattern: ⁻1, ⁻2, ⁻3, ⁻4, . . .

Next number: 72
3. Pattern: ⁺5, ⁺1, ⁺5, ⁺1, . . .
   First number: 5
   Pattern: perfect squares
   First number: 1
4. 201, 301, 401, 501, 601
   50, 48, 53, 52, 50, 55, 54
5. Answers will vary.

Activity 84
1. Input: 24, Output: 10
   Pattern: ÷6
   Initial: 21, Final: 8
   Pattern: ⁺5
2. Entered: heptagon,
   Received: pentagon
   Pattern: ⁻1 side
   Input: 7, Output: 1
   Pattern: multiply by itself (squares)

Activity 85
1. 15 − n   50 ÷ n
2. 12n   n + 21
3. n − 3   n ÷ 8
4. 8n   300n
5. (11 + n) − 13   9n ÷ 5
6. 15 + n
7. 14 − n

Activity 86
1. Set up: 21 + n = 34
   Solution: n = 13 events
2. Set up: $13 − n = $9
   Solution: n = $4
3. Set up: 450 ÷ n = 45
   Solution: n = 10 bags
4. Set up: 6 x 7 = n
   Solution: n = 42 hours
5. Set up: 112 + n = 205
   Solution: n = 93 points

Activity 87
1. Kyle   Jake
2. Carlos   1 cat
3. Brianne   23 pets
4. Cunningham   Yorktown
5. Brownsburg and Yorktown
   Drake

Activity 88
1. pears
2. 2 students
3. 2 students
4. 16 students

5. 5 people
6. 4:00 P.M.
7. 36 people

Activity 89
1. Graph A
2. 10
3. Tuesday
4. Movin' Videos
5. 5 videos
6. both
7. Answers will vary.

Activity 90
1. $^3/_{10}$
2. $^5/_{10} = ^1/_2$
3. $^8/_{10} = ^4/_5$
4. $^5/_{12}$
5. $^{11}/_{12}$
6. $^6/_{12} = ^1/_2$

Activity 91
1. Mean: 12, Median: 11, Mode: 11
   Mean: 12, Median: 12, Mode: 16
2. Mean: 7.5, Median: 9, Mode: 1, 12
   Mean: 26, Median: 22, Mode: 22
3. 84
4. 22 lbs

Activity 92
1. 44   100
2. 16   3
3. 20
4. 9

Activity 93
1. 16 combinations
   sandals in small box, sandals in medium box, sandals in medium-large box, sandals in large box
   tennis shoes in small box, tennis shoes in medium box, tennis shoes in medium-large box, tennis shoes in large box
   boots in small box, boots in medium box, boots in medium-large box, boots in large box
   dress shoes in small box, dress shoes in medium box, dress shoes in medium-large box, dress shoes in large box

2. 10 combinations
   large black, large white, large brown, large striped, large plaid small black, small white, small brown, small striped, small plaid
3. 25 ways
   n = necklace, e = earring
   n1 with e1, n1 with e2, n1 with e3, n1 with e4, n1 with e5
   n2 with e1, n2 with e2, n2 with e3, n2 with e4, n2 with e5
   n3 with e1, n3 with e2, n3 with e3, n3 with e4, n3 with e5
   n4 with e1, n4 with e2, n4 with e3, n4 with e4, n4 with e5
   n5 with e1, n5 with e2, n5 with e3, n5 with e4, n5 with e5

Activity 94
1. 8, 9, 10, 11, 12
2. 1 cracker, 1 mint, 1 lip balm; 2 crackers, 1 mint; 2 crackers, 1 lip balm; 2 mints, 1 cracker; 2 mints, 1 lip balm; 2 lip balms, 1 cracker; 2 lip balms, 1 mint
3. M,M; M,N; M,P; M,K; M,L; N,N; N,P; N,K; N,L; P,P; P,K; P,L; K,K; K,L; LL

Activity 95
1. $^1/_2$
2. $^1/_2$
3. $^2/_{10}$ or $^1/_5$
4. 18
5. $^3/_8$

Activity 96
1. $^2/_5$
2. $^3/_{11}$
3. $^3/_{11}$
4. $^1/_4$
5. $^1/_{10}$
6. $^1/_2$

Activity 97—Practice Test
1. 5,284,026.09
2. $^9/_{100}$
3. 0.4
4. 11
5. $7.16
6. 120
7. $1^2/_5$
8. 18.85

Activity 98—Practice Test
1. associative
2. 168
3. 64 coins
4. $^1/_3$
5. 64,000
6. 61,000
7. 366
8. 54

Activity 99—Practice Test
1. $3^5/_8$ in.
2. 189 cu m
3. 7 hours
4. 83 g
5. 58 cm, 168 sq cm
6. May 16
7. 6
8. octagon

Activity 100—Practice Test
1. (1, 3)
2.
3. $5n = 75$
4. 9 and 6
5. 13, 11
6. 15
7. right
8. $^2/_5$